MUSHROOMS
AND OTHER FUNGI
THEIR FORM AND COLOUR

BY H. KLEIJN

PRESIDENT OF THE ROYAL SOCIETY OF NATURAL HISTORY

IN AMSTERDAM

WITH 94 COLOUR PHOTOGRAPHS

TAKEN IN NATURAL SURROUNDINGS

BY G. D. SWANENBURG DE VEYE

1965

DOUBLEDAY & COMPANY, INC.

GARDEN CITY, NEW YORK

PRINTED IN THE NETHERLANDS BY
JOH. ENSCHEDÉ EN ZONEN GRAFISCHE INRICHTING N.V., HAARLEM
PAPER SUPPLIED BY G. H. BÜHRMANN'S PAPIERGROOTHANDEL N.V., AMSTERDAM
LAY-OUT AND TYPOGRAPHY BY H. CLEWITS
SET IN SPECTRUM
BOUND BY VAN RIJMENAM N.V., 'S-GRAVENHAGE

© 1961 BY H. J. W. BECHT'S UITGEVERSMAATSCHAPPIJ N.V., AMSTERDAM
ENGLISH TEXT © 1962 BY OLDBOURNE BOOK CO. LTD., LONDON
PUBLISHED BY DOUBLEDAY & COMPANY, INC., GARDEN CITY, NEW YORK

No part of this book may be reproduced in any form,
by print, photoprint, microfilm, or any other means
without written permission from the publishers

LIBRARY OF CONGRESS CATALOG CARD NO. 62-7653

QK
617
.K55
1962a

INTRODUCTION

Many books and booklets have already been written about mushrooms and other fungi, either for beginners or for advanced students, or for purely scientific reasons. The authors have used various techniques to illustrate their works, making use of the possibilities available at the time of their compilation, and these range from black-and-white drawings to coloured reproductions. A long-cherished dream of the author has at last been realised with the appearance of this book, a dream which had to wait until now. For the tremendous development in colour photography in recent years, as well as improved printing techniques, has at last made it possible to illustrate in colour a great many kinds of fungi *in their natural surroundings for the first time.*

It is not necessary to be a mycologist to be captivated by the beauty of this treasure chest of shapes and colours. Many, however, who glance at the illustrations in this book may not believe that all these fungi can be discovered by the average layman. The various kinds illustrated can be found mostly everywhere, and a little trouble will disclose them in their natural habitat. Stress must be laid on these natural surroundings, for fungi show preference for certain ground or subsoil in which or on which to grow. After all, one does not look for water lilies on a moor! A stroll through a fir-wood will, generally speaking, reveal different sorts of fungi from those growing in a field or meadow. An extreme example is the Larch Boletus, which is found growing only beneath larches. The various kinds described have been arranged as far as possible according to the ground on which they appear or the subsoil on which they grow. There are naturally some kinds which of necessity have to be satisfied with surroundings and subsoils differing from their normal choice.

There is really no great difficulty in hunting for mushrooms according to shape or colour; all we need to do is to keep a good lookout. A walk or two will be sufficient training to enable ever more kinds to be "discovered." Interest is aroused, and one wonders why these fungi were not noticed before.

This book does not give detailed classifications, but rather a clear description of each kind. The wording has been kept as simple as possible without losing sight of the characteristic properties of the fungi described. Perfection would be attained if the illustrations could speak for themselves, but unfortunately a photograph cannot reproduce in its entirety how to differentiate several kinds. It has not been possible, for technical reasons, to reproduce in colour all the species in their exact size. The descriptive texts give details in this respect.

Apart from form or colour, certain fungi attract attention by their distinctive scent. Some

5

175610

WILLIAM D. McINTYRE LIBRARY
WISCONSIN STATE UNIVERSITY - EAU CLAIRE

smell of aniseed, coal gas, soap, flour, radishes, chlorine, cod-liver oil, bitter almonds, and even of rotten fish. Their taste is also of interest; it can be sharp, peppery, or mild. Even their feel has its contribution to make, for one kind is velvety, another greasy. So far four of the five senses have been considered; what of the fifth? Can mushrooms be heard? This is possible—given perfect circumstances—whenever the spores of a certain large fungus are shot out. The spores not only escape in a cloudlet, but a soft rustle can be heard. The best way to experience this is to gather either the large orange or brown cup toadstool. Both are bowl-shaped with diameters up to 3 inches. A tap on the toadstool when it has reached maturity will make it possible both to see and hear the discharge of the spores.

All these things make hunting for fungi a pure joy; much greater than might have been expected from these "children of darkness."

In addition to the description of the various kinds, this book naturally contains something of the nature and being of this interesting group of plants. Several mushrooms can at first sight be confused with each other. Whenever this is likely to happen, attention is drawn to it. This is particularly necessary with regard to poisonous varieties. The emphasis in this book does not rest so much on which are edible or the contrary; if mushrooms are collected only for their food value, further study must be given to this aspect, for the saying *learn before you eat* is here most important.

Once most of the kinds illustrated have been detected and correctly identified, the next step will be to wish to learn about others. One should then attempt to classify them.

However, in a book whose aim is to give a clear picture, some restrictions have to be imposed. Purposely, only a relatively few fungi, of all classes, have been discussed in this book, so as to provide those interested with a sort of signpost. The writer is convinced (after leading many fungi-hunting excursions) that the general wish of his companions has been first of all to become acquainted with a small number of kinds, and learn to know them well, in order later to go deeper into mycology itself.

All the fungi mentioned have English names; but it is useful to learn their scientific Latin names. It does not lie within the province of this book to enter into the question of which Latin nomenclature to follow. In addition to the present scientific name, the older one is mentioned whenever it differs. The reason for this is that older books use only the original name, and confusion might arise. To facilitate correct pronunciation, the accent is indicated. The Latin specific names will be found in a separate list, as these often point to a certain property, characteristic of the kind, whether it be the colour, the smell, the form, and so on. In the classification these characteristics have been mentioned, so that no microscope is necessary. A good magnifying glass, with magnification 6 to 15 times, will always be useful. A common error is to suppose that mushrooms can be found only in the autumn. In June and July several kinds appear, not to speak of the spring fungi, which are, of course, much earlier.

The author augurs a good harvest for you, but does not forget to warn you to bring home only as few as may be considered necessary. Others coming after you will also want to enjoy these interesting products of nature. The ideal method is to go out and photograph them oneself . . . in colour!

The writer also wishes to record his thanks to the publishers for the lavish way in which his wishes have been met in regard to make-up and reproductions. He is equally grateful to Professor Dr. K. B. Boedijn, Dr. R. A. Maas Geesteranus, and Dr. A. Jaarsveld, who by word and deed have helped him. G. D. Swanenburg de Veye needs a special mention for his admirable co-operation and for having taken all the photographs but one.

CONTENTS

THE FUNGI IN HISTORY

What precisely is a fungus? We now know some of the answers, but much remains to be discovered. What did people in earlier times think? With the knowledge available to them, what was their explanation of the origin of these plants?

Fungi must have been known quite early in man's evolution. Then the only yardstick for a plant, fruit, or toadstool was whether or not it could be used as food. Both cave dweller and huntsman cannot have ignored the fungi. Unfortunately no evidence survives from Sumerian, Babylonian, or similar sources to enable us to appreciate their knowledge; did they eat fungi or had they an aversion to them? What is thought to be a painting of a toadstool has recently been discovered on a mural from the tomb of Amenemhep, dating from about 1450 B.C. References are found in the Bible to lower forms of fungi, such as "rust in the corn," but not to the higher forms that are dealt with in this book.

To learn more about these organisms we must turn to the classics: to the Greeks and the Romans. There were then no treatises on the manner of growth, the construction of fungi, or the like. Plants were considered either as food or medicine, and fungi were no exception. Fungi are mentioned by the satirists Martial and Juvenal—they sing the praises of a dish of well-prepared mushrooms. This is not surprising, since the epicurean Romans valued fungi only as food. The Greeks, more familiar with science than the Romans, are a better source of information. The Greek doctor Hippocrates, born about 460 B.C., is the first to supply some details. While he details his use of fungi in his medical practice, he unfortunately gives no description of the plants themselves.

Theophrastus (c. 372–287 B.C.), called the "Father of Biology," succeeded Aristotle as head of the Athens Lyceum and wrote a *Historia plantarum (peri phytôn historia)*. Through this work he became known as the first biologist to investigate along purely scientific lines. He considered fungi as plants, and although many now think his belief to have been correct, for centuries after him quite other opinions prevailed. He writes: "Although they possess neither roots, stems, leaves, nor fruit, fungi yet belong to the plant world. Roots, which differ greatly amongst plants, are nonexistent in the truffle (*hydnon*), the mushroom (*mykes*), the puffball (*pezis*) and another (unidentified) truffle (*keaunion*)." It is now impossible to determine exactly which fungi he meant. Is *pezis* our Giant Puffball? How correct his observation of these plants was is evidenced by the following quotation: "It is wrong to label all parts of a plant below the surface as roots; the truffle is wholly a plant." Compare with this, for example, the theory of a sixteenth-century biologist who maintained that the truffle was the product of the semen of rutting deer! This

1a. DEATH CAP. *Amani'ta phalloi'des* (Vaill. ex Fr.) Secr.

This toadstool claims the lion's share of fatal poisonings. One wonders why people so often take it home, mistaking it for an edible species. Is it because it grows in thicket clearings, or is it because of its colour, sometimes whitish, which leads one to take it for an edible mushroom? Do gatherers overlook its distinctive features: the swollen base with its sheath and the ring round the stalk? Or, in their haste to take as many home as possible, are they merely careless?

The cap of this fungus is up to 4¾ inches in diameter, rounded at first, later expanding. The colour is very variable: grey-green, yellowish green, bronze-green, olive-green, or fading almost to white. The upper surface of the cap is usually streaked with dark fibrils. It is smooth or with a very few whitish scales; shiny in dry weather, it becomes viscid in damp conditions. The gills are free from the stem and white in colour, with often a faint greenish tinge. The stem, up to 4¼ inches long, is white, usually with a hint of green, and grows thicker towards the base. Around the stem is a thin crinkled and streaked ring. The base of the stem is swollen and enclosed in a lobed sheath.

The Death Cap appears in summer and autumn in deciduous and mixed forests, especially in the neighbourhood of oaks and oak timber.

There seems to be little point in drawing attention to possible confusion of the Death Cap with other toadstools. Instead one should familiarise oneself with the distinctive features of the whole *Amanita* genus. Here they are again, in brief: white gills, ringed stem with a bulb or sheath at the base, cap often with small adhesions. It is also advisable to acquaint oneself with the characteristics of the well-known Fly Agaric, also belonging to the genus *Amanita*.

1b. PANTHER CAP or FALSE BLUSHER. *Amani'ta pantheri'na* (DC. ex Fr.) Secr.

This species has very poisonous properties, and, for beginners, confusion with other species is by no means impossible. It contains, among other poisons, some that affect the nervous system; i.e., muscarine, muscaridine, and choline. Because the symptoms of poisoning occur very soon after eating, it is possible to take timely action. It is not, as is the Death Cap, a deadly poisonous variety.

The cap, up to 4 inches in diameter, may vary in colour from greyish brown to umber or olive-brown and is decorated with concentric circles of white patches. The margin is striped. The gills are white, rather closely set together, and disconnected from the stalk. The slender stem, up to 5 inches long, rises from a swollen base. Above the swelling are one or two indistinct scaly rings. The Panther Cap resembles two other non-poisonous species of *Amanita*: the Blusher (*A. rubes'cens* [Pers. ex Fr.] S. F. Gray), and the Grey Amanita (*A. spis'sa* [Fr.] Quel.). The Blusher is distinguished by its more reddish-brown cap. It has patches, but there are no stripes on the margin of the cap. The flesh of the cap and stem is reddish, especially at the base of the stem. The Grey Amanita has a greyish-brown cap with white patches and a whitish striped sleeve. Its stalk ends in a rimless, somewhat rooting "bulb."

1c. GRISETTE. *Amani'ta ful'va* Schaeff. ex Pers., syn. *Amani'ta (Amanitop'sis) vagina'ta* var. *fulva* Bull.

This toadstool was formerly classed by mycologists as *Amanitopsis vaginata*, with different varieties according to colour. Thus a var. *plumbea* was recognised, with a grey cap. In the opinion of many modern mycologists, the var. *plumbea* should be called *Amanita vaginata* (Bull. ex Fr.) Quel., and the former *A. vaginata* should be called *Amanita fulva* Schaeff. This is the slenderest species of *Amanita*. The thinly fleshed cap is reddish brown with very few patches and with a milled edge. The cap is first bell-shaped, later more expanded, sometimes with a slight bulge in the middle. The gills are white and set close together. The slender stem, up to 6 inches long, is hollow and very brittle and grows gradually thinner between base and cap.

clearly shows how erroneous were the beliefs about fungi two thousand years after Theophrastus. In the section dealing with odours, Theophrastus observes: "Though some mushrooms grow on manure, they do not partake of the medium on which they stand and they remain scentless." It is probable that he is referring to the familiar edible mushroom (*champignon de couche*), though one cannot be certain. He also contests the opinion that fungi bear fruit. From these and various facts, it is clear that the learned Greek was an excellent observer, and that furthermore he first made sure of his facts before committing them to writing.

A remarkable conclusion of his was that fungi fossilised by the heat of the sun were to be found on the shores of the Red Sea. At first sight this is a scarcely credible theory, but it is not wholly due to the fantasy of Theophrastus. Even today we know the "mushroom stone" found in Italy and other countries bordering the shores of the Mediterranean. In Italy it is called "pietra fungaia," its scientific name being *Polyporus tuberaster* Jacq. ex Fr. It has also, though rarely, been found in northern Europe and in Canada; it usually flourishes only in warmer regions. What is the truth about this unusual type? Does the fungus really spring from a stone? Like all fungi, this tuberaster originates from spawn (mycelium). The difference in this case, however, is that the threads have compacted and become a hard mass, giving at first sight the impression of a piece of stone. Similar structures occur in various sorts of fungi and may be considered as organs of food reserve. Whenever circumstances of climate and humidity are favourable, the fungus can grow out of this hard mass of "stone."

Pliny the Elder (A.D. 23–A.D. 79) made several references to the origin and appearance of fungi and also to their poisonous qualities and to cases of poisoning. This Roman scholar's observations in the fields of natural history, geology, and astronomy have given us an insight into the standards of science in his day. He was actually more of a compiler than a scientific investigator. He claims in his writings that fungi spring from mud and the sour sap of damp earth, or from the roots of oak. He calculated the length of the mushroom's life as 7 days from birth to death. Has the mystical significance of the figure 7 anything to do with this theory? Truffles, which he also mentions, are given a longer life span—a maximum of one year. According to Pliny, fungi on trees grow out of the sap of the trees. He concludes that all varieties owe their existence to rain, so he must have noticed the increase in toadstools after rain. He gives advice on how to differentiate between edible and poisonous kinds of fungi—in his day many species were eaten, a fact confirmed in Martial's epigrams. The criteria Pliny used to determine the toxicity or edibility were, however, not sound, and one gets the impression that he quoted popular sentiment with all its accretions. He asserts, for instance, that fungi growing near snake pits are poisonous. Rusted iron and rags, in his opinion, were hardly likely to produce edible varieties of mushrooms. Such opinions were held for centuries, and many an old herbal repeats Pliny's

2. DRYAD'S SADDLE. *Polyp'orus squamo'sus* Huds. ex Fr., syn. *Mela'nopus squamo'sus* (Huds. ex Fr.) Pat.

This is one of our largest and most attractive fungi, with ochre-yellow cap and brown scales arranged roughly in concentric circles. With its many pores it can produce an enormous number of spores in the course of a year. A. H. R. Buller has worked out experimentally that a big saddle fungus produces 50,000,000,000 spores. This fungus is not particular in its choice of host and can be found on many kinds of trees: beech, elm, chestnut, lime, willow, etc. Quite early in the year (May), young specimens can be seen as conical knobs on various parts of the tree.

The Dryad's Saddle may reach a diameter of 24 inches. Several are usually found together, overlapping one another like tiles. The cap is adorned with closely set triangular brown scales. It is fan-shaped to semicircular and somewhat depressed near the stem. The pores run down the stem and are at first whitish, later yellowish to light brown. The stem, situated to one side near the edge, is short and thick, growing darker towards the base.

ancient beliefs. In an herbal by P. A. Matthiolus, written in the sixteenth century, these beliefs are both described and illustrated.

Pliny is considerably more explicit regarding truffles. He looks upon them with wonder because they grow without any root and yet live. He did notice that the truffle was surrounded by hairlike threads and he called them "capilla mentis," not realising that these were mycelium threads and in fact part of the plant itself. It is not surprising that Pliny paid so much attention to truffles, for rich Romans were very fond of them as well as of other kinds of fungi. Both Martial and Juvenal mention this fact. Martial (A.D. 40–A.D. 102) writes in his Satires:

Argentum atque aurum facile est, laenam togamque mittere;
Boletus mittere difficile est.

Freely translated, Martial writes that it is easy to despise gold and silver but very hard to leave a plate of mushrooms untouched. Although Martial uses the word "boletus" in his verse, he was not referring to the genus *Boletus*, in which we group a certain number of edible toadstools. *Boletus* has tubes beneath its cap while the Imperial Mushroom of ancient Rome (*Amanita caesarea*) has gills. It looks at first sight like the Fly Agaric (*A. muscaria*), from which it can be distinguished by the absence of white patches on the cap and the greater yellowness of the gills and stalk. *A. caesarea* is found in southern Europe, the Mediterranean countries, and in North America.

This much-esteemed edible mushroom was greatly favoured by patrician families and merchants of ancient Rome and was called "Cibus deorum"—the food of the gods.

What is now termed a boletus was named *suillus* by Roman writers. It is difficult to determine which particular type of boletus was understood by that name, as no closer description of it has survived. It has been suggested that the *suillus* was the Squirrel's Bread (*Boletus edulis*) on the following grounds: *suillus* means pig, and in all probability such a name was used, since both domestic pigs and the half-wild swine kept by the Romans were fond of this fungus. Furthermore, this same *B. edulis* is in Italy called "porcino" or "bole porcino"—the same expression "pig" (porcino) also occurring. This coincidence is striking and certainly gives ground for the conjecture.

Another much-esteemed fungus was the truffle—called *tubera* by the Romans—a delicacy which is today still greatly appreciated. Juvenal's *Satires* mentions that the African truffle was widely known and much in demand—so much so that Juvenal has Alledius exclaim that he prefers truffles to wheat. In another of his satires Juvenal refers to a kitchen-maid who had learnt to prepare a particularly pleasing dish and could peel the truffles and clean the boletus

3a. NARCISSUS BLEWIT. *Tricholo'ma sulphu'reum* (Bull. ex Fr.) Kummer.

This Blewit is easy to recognise by its uniform sulphur-yellow colour and its offensive smell, which can best be compared with the smell of coal gas or sulphur dioxide (according to some experts, with the smell of narcissus bulbs, *Narcissus jonquilla*, or syringa).

The flesh is also yellow. The cap, 1¼ to 2½ inches, is sulphur-yellow with a darker, brownish centre. It is irregularly lumpy and feels like chamois leather.

The gills are yellow and distantly spaced. The stem is usually curved, yellow, and fibrously striated. This toadstool grows in deciduous forests and also in mixed woods from late summer until autumn.

Confusion may be possible with the Yellow Knight Fungus (*Tricholoma flavovirens* [Pers. ex Fr.] Lundell, syn. *Tricholoma equestre* [L. ex Fr.] Kummer). This latter species does not possess an unpleasant smell and usually appears in sandy pinewoods. The cap tends to an olive colour or to a green-yellow, is better fleshed, sticky (shiny when dry), and covered with tiny fibrils. The gills, however, are sulphur-yellow. The stem is not so slender as that of the Narcissus Blewit. It often grows more or less sunk into the ground.

3b. RED CURTAIN FUNGUS. *Cortina'rius bola'ris* (Pers. ex Fr.) Fr., syn. *Inolo'ma bola're* (Pers. ex Fr.) Ricken.

The cap, 1¼ to 2½ inches, is closely covered with wine-red scales growing on a loam-coloured background. The closely set gills are pale but later turn the colour of cinnamon. The fibrous stem is not thickened and has the same colour as the cap, though it may be more yellow with red fibrils. This beautiful Curtain Fungus is not common but may be found in deciduous woods, especially beech woods.

A peculiarity of the Curtain fungi (Cortinariaceae) is the existence of a velum partiale in a young stage. This velum, not a membrane as we find in the young amanites, can be observed as a thread-like or cobweb-like curtain (cortina) between the edge of the cap and the stem. When the toadstool ages, the cortina tears loose and its remains can be found at the edge of the cap and as a ring around the stem.

The spores are of a pale rusty colour.

The Curtain Fungus grows exclusively on the ground.

3c. LILAC THICKFOOT or LILAC CURTAIN FUNGUS. *Cortina'rius albo-viola'ceus* (Pers. ex Fr.) Fr., syn. *Inolo'ma albo-viola'ceum* (Pers. ex Fr.) Ricken.

The Lilac Thickfoot is one of the bigger species amongst the numerous varieties of the Curtain fungi. It has a cap width from 1¼ to 4 inches. The colour is pink to purple (later fading). In its early stage the smooth, satiny and fleshy cap is bell-shaped with an edge bent inwards; it flattens later in life. The gills are at first violet, then grey-violet, and finally turn ochreous brown. The light violet stem may reach a length of 4 inches and shows the remains of the curtain. It is bulbous at the base and becomes club-shaped as it ages.

The Lilac Curtain Fungus is rather common and can be found between oak and beech leaves in summer and late autumn.

3d. MIST FUNGUS. *Clitocy'be nebula'ris* (Batsch. ex Fr.) Kummer.

Mist Fungus is a felicitous name because the cap has a grey to mist-like colour, which is also indicated by the Latin specific name *nebularis*—mist colour. This Gill fungus belongs to the genus of Funnel fungi (*Clitocybe*). Although it deviates somewhat from the typical funnel shape, it has the decurrent gills. A characteristic species of this genus is the Slender Funnel Fungus, described on page 90. The Mist Fungus, one of the largest among Funnel fungi, has a smooth cap, 2¾ to 6 inches wide, is fleshy in the centre, and has a light grey to ashy colour with often a lighter-coloured margin. The cap appears to be covered with hoarfrost in its early stage. It is spherical in shape, vaulted with an inrolled edge; this later spreads out, with a more or less depressed centre and, as a rule, a wavy edge. The gills, crowded, short, and decurrent, are white to yellowish. The stout stem, 2½ to 4 inches long, has a lighter colour than the cap; it is fibrous and striped, usually bulbous at the base and white and felty in texture.

The flesh neither smells nor tastes agreeable. The Mist Fungus appears late in the year, not before autumn, but can still be found in November, especially in deciduous woods, usually growing in groups or in fairy rings.

The specimens illustrated, photographed after a shower, show a part of such a fairy ring. Confusion may occur with the Club Funnel Fungus (*Clitocybe clavipes* [Pers. ex Fr.] Kummer), which usually grows in pinewoods. This latter species (size up to 2¾ inches) is smaller, has a grey-brown cap, decurrent gills, and a characteristic porous club-shaped stem. When the flesh is pressed in the centre of the cap of the Club Funnel, it feels spongy and is less firm than that of the Mist Fungus.

without help. The *tubera* of the Romans is without doubt the proper truffle; this is confirmed by others, including Pliny, who described various kinds. The scientific name for the truffle is *Tuber*.

The reverence for certain mushrooms as delicacies went so far in Roman times that the Emperor Tiberius promised to pay an exorbitant price for a poem glorifying the boletus. Mushrooms were cleaned with an amber knife and served in special dishes called *boletarii*. The only known recipe manual of the period—and Europe's oldest cookery book—is that of Caelius Apicius. The book was written in the third century A.D. by a certain Caelius, to whom the cognomen Apicius was given. Since Apicius was well known as a gourmet, his name was added to recommend the work. Many recipes are given for the preparation of fungi for the table.

Plutarch also refers to these *tuberae terrae*, as Pliny called them. Pliny distinguishes three kinds, which have been identified as follows:

Tuber colore nigro as *Tuber brumale* and *Tuber melanospermum*
Tuber colore intus candide as *Tuber magnatum*
Tuber colore rufe as *Tuber rufum*

These proper truffles are not generally found in Britain or North America, but they would be called black, white, and red truffles.

A Greek doctor, Pedanios Dioscorides, born in Anazarba in Cilicia and who lived about A.D. 50, was a soldier in Nero's army and wrote a long five-part book on medical remedies (*De Materia medica*). He does not throw much light on fungi, and his views as to their toxicity do not differ much from those of Pliny. He mentions that non-poisonous toadstools were much in demand for the seasoning of sauces, but that they could be harmful if used in quantity; an opinion to which we may still subscribe, since toadstools contain certain substances difficult to digest.

As a doctor, Dioscorides also gives remedies for those who indulged too freely in a dish of fungi and thereby suffered from colic. He prescribes a salt-water enema; he further recommends chicken dung dissolved in vinegar and mixed with honey. He also knew one medicinal fungus, which was still much used centuries later: the *Polyporus officinalis*. The specific name *officinalis* indicates its pharmaceutical use. Dioscorides called it Agarikon, and Pliny referred to it as Agaricus. In the old herbals the larch fungus is called Agaricus, and in many prescriptions up to late in the eighteenth century agaricum is to be found. Nor was it ever absent from the stock of chemists of those times. It is a wood fungus found on the larch trees in Mediterranean countries. In W. Turner's Herbal (1551) we find the remark: "Ye famous medice called Agarick."

Although neither Hippocrates nor Galen shed any new light on fungi, their writings were

4a. YELLOW CRUST FUNGUS. *Ste'reum hirsu'tum* (Willd. ex Fr.) Fr.

As indicated by its name, this fungus grows like an elastic, tenacious, yellow crust on stumps, branches, poles, and trunks of foliage trees. This species of the *Stereum* genus has a curved cap standing out from the wood, with a woolly, yellow-white to ashy-coloured upperside. There are also specimens which grow almost completely pressed close to the wood. In such specimens the cap is hardly noticeable. The Yellow Crust Fungus can be found growing separately—up to a few inches—but also in merging patches or tile-wise. The smooth hymenium is yellow to ochre. It is very common and can be found almost throughout the year.

When you find a fungus of identical shape and appearance but with purple hymenium, then you have identified the Purple Crust Fungus (*Stereum purpureum* [Pers. ex Fr.] Fr.). Both species belong to the Crust fungi (Corticiaceae).

4b. BLACK STUD FUNGUS. *Phaeobulga'ria in'quinans* (Pers. ex Fr.) Nannf., syn. *Bulga'ria in'-quinans* Pers. ex Fr., *Bulga'ria polymor'pha* Wettst.

This tiny fungus belongs to the Cup fungi (Discomycetes) and is common on dead wood, oaks in particular, practically throughout the year. It is not a showy species, but the mature specimen is of striking appearance with its shiny coal-black upper surface.

The fungus—½ to 1½ inches wide—is globular at first but gradually spreads out into something resembling a stud or top. It has a dark brown exterior, and the upper surface is slimy and coal-black. The stalk is very short or sometimes tends to disappear completely. The shape, colour, and the way in which it grows in bunches on dead oak wood make this species easy to identify.

4c. HELMET MYCENA. *Myce'na galericula'ta* (Scop. ex Fr.) S. F. Gray.

From early in the year until well into autumn this common *Mycena* can be found on or near stumps and trunks; very often it grows in clusters.

The cap, which may be up to 2½ inches wide, is cone- to bell-shaped but later flattens out. It has a grey to ashy-brown colour. The somewhat tough and bare cap is usually rugosely striped. The close gills are whitish but become pinkish later. The smooth and shining stalk—up to 4 inches—is ashy and usually haired at the base. As a rule, the base of the stem is root-like and extended into the mouldered wood.

A fungus almost identical with this species and hence often confused with it is the Striped Stalk Mycena (*Mycena polygramma* [Bull. ex Fr.] S. F. Gray) growing on much the same sites. This latter species is differentiated by the more bluish-grey to silver-grey colour of its stalk, which has also lengthwise stripes (use a magnifying glass); the gills are whitish and rarely turn pinkish later on.

4d. BIG BLOODSTALK. *Myce'na haemato'pus* (Pers. ex Fr.) Kummer.

Amongst the graceful bell-shaped Mycenas there are some kinds—Lactipedes—which secrete a coloured, aqueous fluid when the stalk is broken. (Squeeze it lightly!) The Big Bloodstalk has a dark blood-red secretion, the Little Bloodstalk (*Mycena sanguinolenta* [Alb. & Schw. ex Fr.] Kummer) secretes a watery purple to blood-red fluid, whereas the Milkstalk (*Mycena galopus* [Pers. ex Fr.] Kummer) has a milk-white fluid. The Big Bloodstalk grows in clusters on mouldered wood and fallen branches; the Little Bloodstalk between moss and needles in deciduous woods and pinewoods; the Milkstalk in much the same places as the Little Bloodstalk. The description of the Big Bloodstalk is as follows: The blunt bell-shaped to conical cap is at first greyish, later turning purple to auburn; the edge of the cap is striated and indented. The gills are whitish to pink. The stalk, up to 2½ inches, is purple brown to ruddy.

The Little Bloodstalk: cap ¼ to ¾ inches, cone-shaped, light brownish red with a lighter and striated margin. Gills are whitish with a brownish-red edge (under a magnifying glass). The stalk is thin, smooth, grey-brown, and up to 4 inches in length. It can be found between moss and needles in pinewoods and deciduous woods until well into autumn.

Milkstalk: cap ¼ inch, ashy to dark black-brown (often white), conical with a striated margin. Gills white. Stalk up to 3½ inches in length. It can be found in deciduous woods and pinewoods; also on stumps of trees.

nonetheless considered so important that for centuries afterwards the scientific world accepted what they had written. For an opinion to carry weight it needed only to be prefaced by "Galenus dixit," the intention being that, as Galen had said it, all further discussion was useless.

In medieval writings such as those of Hildegard von Bingen, Abbess of St. Ruprechtsberg by Bingen, short remarks regarding toadstools are found, but they give little further information. The famous Arabian doctor, Avicenna, gives us his view on how to separate the good from the poisonous fungi, as well as the methods to be used in cases of toadstool poisoning. He writes that black or green toadstools, together with those the colours of peacocks, are toxic. These vague details give us nothing to go on. It is quite useless to rely on the colour of a mushroom to determine whether or not it is poisonous. It is possible, however, that in the course of his practice Avicenna learnt the deadly properties of the green *Amanita phalloides* and therefore assumed all green mushrooms to be deadly. Or was it the verdigris colour that frightened him?

Albertus Magnus (1193–1280), sometimes called Adalbert the Great, added, as a result of research, his own views to those generally accepted. He expressed the opinion that mushrooms were not strictly plants but only excrescences of earth and plants; that is why, he says, they are generally brittle and some are poisonous owing to the rotting dampness on which they originate. That, too, he thought, explained their short life span.

He also knew that the Fly Agaric (*Amanita muscaria*) was poisonous, and adds some picturesque details to this information: if this agaric is steeped in milk, the flies which alight on this mixture and taste it swell up and die. The name Fly Agaric has therefore a venerable ancestry, as well as its property of killing flies—which resides mostly in its red cap. This manner of killing flies is still practiced in some parts of Europe. The cap, or the red skin of the cap, is placed on a saucer in sweetened milk to attract and kill flies.

Albertus Magnus, Count of Bollstädt, nicknamed Doctor Universalis, also gives advice against poisoning, or methods to reduce the effects of poisoning. Unfortunately he still falls prey to the fables that poisonous mushrooms originate from rotting material grown on serpents' nests, snake holes, or rusty iron. He does, however, give us some information on truffles, which have continued to be regarded as delicacies throughout the ages.

It is not until the sixteenth century that we find evidence of interest in fungi beyond what was to be discovered in contemporary herbals. Hermolaus, Ruellius, and Matthiolus, all botanists, have been called the fathers of mycology; they brought additions and emendations to the works of their predecessors. Hermolaus, a Venetian, proposed in 1526 (in a commentary on the five books of Dioscorides) a table of classification of fungi then known. He divided them into various groups, such as:

Fungi ovati — Fungi digitelli — Fungi spongiati

25

5a. ORANGE VEIN FUNGUS. *Phle'bia radia'ta* Fr. ex Donk., syn. *Phle'bia auranti'aca* (Sow. ex Fr.) Schroet.

Many kinds of fungi are lignicolous, growing exclusively on wood. Amongst other genera, we have species of *Clavaria, Flammula, Hypholoma, Mycena, Pholiota, Tremella, Xylaria,* and the various genera of the large group of Perforated fungi (Polyporaceae) and the Crust fungi (Corticiaceae).

The Orange Vein Fungus, which belongs to the latter group, has beautiful orange-red to flesh-coloured flesh with occasionally a light purple tint. It grows in waxy, knotty slices or crusts which are circular in shape and generally covered with folds and veins, radially arranged. In many cases parts of these crusts merge, depending on the wood on which it grows.

For the greater part of the year this fungus can be found on branches and stems of either living or dead conifers and broad-leaved trees, although it does not appear everywhere. It may spread on the ground on twigs and moss.

5b. HORN OF PLENTY. *Craterel'lus cornucopioi'des* (L. ex Fr.) Pers.

The name Horn of Plenty has undoubtedly a more pleasant sound than the German appellation *Totentrompete* (Trumpet of Death). This mushroom may reach a height of 6 inches and is striking more for its shape—horn or funnel—than for its colour, which is predominantly dark.

The young plant is smooth, covered with hymenium, but later becomes creased. The outside has an ashy colour which may temporarily lighten because of the spores, and the inside may vary from black-brown to black. This fungus has a hollow stem, and the flesh is thin and rather tough. The hollow fruit-body has a wavy edge which is turned back. Any further description of this characteristic species would be superfluous.

The Horn of Plenty appears mostly in local groups from summer to late autumn and is found in deciduous forests (beeches and oaks) and pinewoods, but is by no means common. This species belongs to the group called the Cantharellaceae, to which also belongs the well-known Chanterelle (*Cantharellus cibarius* Fr.).

5c. YELLOW PRICKLE FUNGUS. *Hy'dnum repan'dum* L. ex Fr.

With the exception of the little Earspoon Fungus (*Auriscalpium vulgare*) (see page 78), which is remarkable for growing on pine cones, only some big species of the Prickle toadstools (Hydnaceae) can be easily identified, such as the above-mentioned species.

It has a fleshy cap of a pale yellow to yellow-orange colour, up to 4¾ inches in diameter. At first the cap is irregular and spherical in shape, but it flattens later on, the lobed edge curling inwards. The brittle thorns running down the stem differ in length and, though whitish to yellowish at first, they have the same colour as the cap in the full-grown specimen. The short and usually eccentric stalk is of a lighter shade than the cap.

The Yellow Prickle toadstool is quite common and grows in groups. From summer to autumn it can be found in deciduous forests and, though less frequently, in pinewoods. Young specimens are edible, but old specimens taste very bitter.

These could be equated with truffles, morels, and boletes. This was indeed a step forward from the earlier division into toxic and non-toxic, but it was no final solution. For this we have to wait another two centuries. Hermolaus grouped together, for instance, all fungi growing on trees, calling them Arborei; those growing in fields and meadows he called Campestres. His endeavours to escape old ideas and myths are praiseworthy.

Matthiolus, an Italian, went one step further and illustrated his works (1560). His drawings, however, still portray fungi with the traditional snake—so the influence of Dioscorides was still present. One of the best writers on the subject at this time was undoubtedly Caesalpinus (1519–1603), who in *De Plantis*, published in 1583, describes clearly various types of fungi. This scholar, philosopher, and doctor was the director of the botanical gardens at Pisa, where he also lectured. Most remarkable is that he considered the whole toadstool as a fruit. Various other scholarly books appeared in which fungi are mentioned. Among these, a note should be made of Carolus Clusius (1525–1609), whose book *Fungorum in Pannoniis observatorum brevis historia*, published in 1601, is famous. He begins by dividing fungi into edible and poisonous varieties and describes various parts of their structure. He puts the various fungi into families and arranges the edible ones in 24 families with 46 sorts, and the poisonous ones into 26 families with 59 sorts. The work is illustrated by many wood cuts, some of which we also find in the herbal *L'Obel;* there we recognise Jew's Ear, Morel, Parasol, and Stinkhorn.

Various botanists after him—among them Loesel, Sterbeeck, Tournefort, and Vaillant—described fungi or tried to list them into a system of nomenclature. The use of the microscope began to make its influence felt, so that as we examine these various works we are struck by the growing understanding of the structure of the fungi. Soon after Vaillant's work appeared (1727) came a book written by a Florentine, P. A. Michaeli (1729), entitled *Nova Plantarum juxta Tournefortii*

An illustration from *Commentarii* by P. A. Matthiolus (1560)

29

6a. STINKHORN. *Phal'lus impudi'cus* L. ex Pers., syn. *Ithyphal'lus impudi'cus* (L. ex Pers.) E. Fischer.

This toadstool belongs to the Puffballs (Gasteromycetes). The name Stinkhorn needs no elaboration, as the smell of this species is recognisable at quite a distance. The development of this Stinkhorn and its relatives is very interesting. When you find a Stinkhorn you should look for a young and undeveloped specimen in close proximity. Such a young Stinkhorn is globular to egg-shaped and can be found just below the surface of the soil, if not partly rising above it. At the bottom of the "egg" you will also find the white mycelium cords. When you dig out the egg, which is the size of a large chicken's egg, you will discover that this "witch's egg" or "devil's egg," as it is also called, is jelly-like and more or less elastic to the touch. Take this "witch's egg" home and place it on moist soil under a bell jar; there is a fair chance that by the next morning you will have a full-grown Stinkhorn. The shape will be as shown in the corresponding picture, and the entire cap will soon be covered with olive-green slime containing spores. The carrion-like smell attracts carrion-loving insects (note the carrion-flies on the left-hand side of the cap). The longitudinal section of an "egg" is given in the picture and shows the folded position of the embryonic toadstool.

The Stinkhorn is very common and can be found in woods (oak), parks, and so on, during summer and autumn.

The porous stalk, up to 6 inches long, is white and hollow and sprouts out of the burst, sheath-like "eggshell." On top of this stalk is the bell-shaped cap with its honeycomb structure; in the first stage it is covered with olive-green slime.

6b. DOG STINKHORN. *Muti'nus cani'nus* (Huds. ex Pers.) Fr., syn. *Phal'lus cani'nus* Huds. ex Pers.

The Dog Stinkhorn develops exactly like the Stinkhorn (see above). The "egg," however, is oval but smaller—up to 1½ inches. This graceful species is easy to recognise. The receptacle is hollow, porous, flabby, cream-coloured, and may fall over easily. The "cap" is covered with dark olive-green spores, containing slime at first, but after this has disappeared the colour becomes buff to orange-red. The carrion smell is less noticeable than that of the Stinkhorn, the latter being recognisable at a great distance.

The Dog Stinkhorn belongs to the Puffballs (Gasteromycetes) and is rather common in all kinds of woods, on or close to stumps of mouldered wood and along paths; it can be found from July to October, often growing in groups.

The dirty-white "eggs" taken home will soon grow out on damp soil, sometimes overnight. The white mycelium cords are easy to observe in this species.

6c. GREEN SLIME FUNGUS. *Leo'tia lu'brica* Pers. ex Fr.

This species may occur in quite different shapes, outer appearances, and colours and can be found growing on moss in all kinds of damp woods and in ditches running through them. As the colour does not usually show up against the place where it is growing, the Green Slime Fungus is often overlooked. The stalk is yellowish to yellow-greenish and the cap yellow-green to brown-olive on top.

This fungus can grow to a height of 2½ inches and is slimy to the touch—especially the cap. This cap is ¾ inch wide, like twisted intestines, with an inrolled edge.

The Green Slime Fungus belongs to the Sac fungi (Ascomycetes) and is fairly common from autumn into winter.

6d. STALKED SAUCER. *Helvel'la macro'pus* (Pers. ex Fr.) P. Karst., syn. *Macropo'dia macro'pus* (Pers. ex Fr.) Fuckel, *Pezi'za macro'pus* Pers. ex Fr.

This graceful species of the Sac fungi (Ascomycetes) is easy to recognise: a stalk with a flat or saucer-like disc on top.

The slender stalk—up to 2¾ inches long—is light grey to dun colour and is rough-haired in texture. On top of it grows a thin flat to saucer-shaped disc—⅞ inch across—of roughly the same colour and hairy surface; the upper part of the saucer, however, is smooth and grey-brown. Because of its colour, this pretty little fungus does not often show up well against the dark soil in the wood.

methodum disposita. Michaeli used a microscope and adapted Tournefort's method of classification. He was on the right path and expresses the opinion that the toadstool comes straight out of a seed. But he had as yet no knowledge of the spawn which originates from the spores and forms the basis for the development of the fruit-body. He experimented by sowing "seeds" of mushrooms and moulds. He used the moulds of the genera *Botrytis, Aspergillus,* and *Mucor* with success and could immediately sow spores again (or seeds, as he called them). For breeding-ground he used pieces of melon, pear, and quince, and notes that he always found that the same sort reproduced itself. With agarics he used old leaves but found that he had to wait longer for the appearance of the fruit-body. When we consider that at that time these experiments could easily have been vitiated by contaminating moulds, it is surprising that such excellent results were obtained. It is not to be wondered that Michaeli did not receive the approval of every botanist, and indeed his book was subjected to heavy criticism, some of it going so far as to deny the vegetable nature of the mushroom. Other well-known mycologists of the eighteenth century were Batsch, Bulliard, Paulot; each of them contributed in his own way to a better understanding of the fruit-body as a spore-producing structure.

With C. H. Persoon (1755–1837) a new era in knowledge of the fungi begins, especially with regard to classification and nomenclature. One of his best-known works, issued in 1801, is *Synopsis methodica fungorum.*

Elias Fries (1794–1878) formulated a system of classification of toadstools based on the colour of the spores. This system still holds good in broad outline, although in the course of years improvements have been made by various mycologists. Fries' first great work, *Systema mycologicum,* appeared in 1821, in which he gave a methodical description of all the then known species. After Elias Fries had published his pioneer work and thus awakened much scientific interest in these "least honoured products of nature," it was only natural that closer study towards a better and deeper understanding of them should result. The corollary was that new species were discovered and described, that some genera were divided, and some species ascribed to other genera; the description of the various kinds of fungi became fuller and clearer, and other criteria were used to differentiate fungus groups from each other. Such criteria are: spore sizes, the form of cystidia and paraphyses, as well as colour reactions to chemical reagents (especially useful in the genus *Russula*).

During the last fifty years a great many mycologists have devoted much time to classification. The study of the sexuality of fungi has also yielded important results, and applied mycology—particularly with regard to the use of the lower fungi as medical remedies—has made great strides in the present century. We must also take into account the attacks made on cultivated plants by various fungi such as Rust. The fight against them is of great economic importance.

7a. BROWN QUIVERING FUNGUS. *Tremel'la folia'cea* Fr.

This species belongs to the family of Quivering Fungi, or Tremellaceae. The fungus may reach a breadth of more than 4 inches and is formed of irregular crinkled wavy lobes, up to ¼ inch thick, which look gelatinous. These are united at the base and firmly attached to the wood on which the fungus grows. At first translucent and light brown to beige, it later turns darker. If dried, it becomes dark brown or blackish. It can later be brought back to its original colour by adding water. The spores are formed all over the fruit-body—that is, the lobes. This fungus can be seen from autumn until late in the year, on branches, trunks, and posts made of pine or other wood.

7b. JEW'S EAR. *Auricula'ria auricu'la-Jud'ae* Fr., syn. *Hirne'ola auricu'la-Jud'ae* (Fr.) Berk.

This species belongs to quite another group than the Red-pored Wood Fungus, also described on this page; it is a member of the Quivering Fungi, or Tremellaceae. A distinguishing feature of these fungi is that when fresh they are of jelly-like consistency, or tough and gelatinous. Just like the ordinary gilled fungi, they belong to the great division of stalked fungi, or Basidiomycetes, although the form deviates considerably from the standard cap and stalk.

The fruit-body of the Jew's Ear varies greatly in form. When young it is more or less bowl-shaped; as it develops it takes the shape of a crimped shell or ear, up to 3¼ inches broad, with a veinlike structure on the inside. The colour, like the shape, may be extremely varied. Specimens found may be reddish brown, browny flesh-coloured, greyish brown, or violet-grey. Several specimens are usually found growing together, and in this case the range of form and colours from the young to the adult plant can be easily seen. It has a clear preference for old elderberry trees but can also be found on oak, beech, and elm. Another peculiarity is that the Jew's Ear, which become hard and horny as it dries, will return to its original state when soaked in water. Do not confuse this species with an old specimen of the Brown Quivering Fungus, which is more sinuous, crinkled, and folded. (See Plate 7a.)

7c. RED-PORED WOOD FUNGUS. *Daeda'lea confrago'sa* (Bolt. ex Fr.) Schroet.

This pore fungus, up to 4¾ inches across, can be found until late in the year on the branches and trunks of deciduous trees. The semicircular cap, firmly attached along its diameter to the wood on which it grows, has a broad base and becomes gradually thinner toward the circumference. The upperside is somewhat felty in texture and divided into darker and lighter colour-ed zones. The underside is furnished with pores that may assume any shape from a circle to a winding maze; frosted with grey at first, it gradually changes to a reddish brown. It is discoloured by pressure. The whole plant is corky. Several different varieties are to be distinguished.

THE ORIGIN OF THE MUSHROOM IN POPULAR BELIEF

Many legends exist concerning the origin of fungi—as is the case with many plants. This is due mainly to the fact that even in books on plant lore so little information on fungi is given. Yet these products of nature have always excited curiosity, particularly amongst country folk. Many tales and legends about toadstools come from eastern Europe and the Balkans. This is not surprising, for in these countries fungi were—and are—of considerable importance as food.

The need for explanation is characteristic of man. He seeks for the origin of phenomena and their interconnection. He demands answers to all questions concerning the world about him. It is from this compulsion that the highest expressions of religion and knowledge have developed.

We shall quote some of the myths and legends and would point out that several variations of these exist, sometimes common to countries far apart. First a legend from the neighbourhood of Leipa in Bohemia. Christ and Peter walked through a village, begging for bread and biscuits to satisfy their hunger. Now and then crusts were thrown to them and so they continued on their way happily enough. They eventually reached a large forest, and as they walked through they munched the bread and biscuits, baked of white and brown flour. Wherever crumbs fell, up sprang a fungus. You will probably have already guessed that the toadstools growing from brown flour were poisonous and inedible, whilst the white flour produced the edible kinds.

In Poland the following tale is popular: Christ and Peter were one day entertained by an old peasant woman who, as they left, gave them each a loaf of bread for their journey. After they had walked some way, Peter became hungry and, dropping a few paces behind Our Lord, bit off a piece of bread. Before he had time to swallow it, Christ turned round to speak to him. Peter had to spit out the bread to reply, and, according to the legend, toadstools grew from the bits of bread that fell to the ground. In variations of this tale, a tart or a cake sometimes replaces the loaf of bread.

These two legends are concerned with the origin of fungi in general, but there are others where a particular species is mentioned. This happens with the well-known Fly Agaric. According to popular belief in Kocevje, southern Yugoslavia, *Amanita muscaria* originated in the foam from the mouth of Wotan's horse. It is quite possible that all these legends had heathen origins and with the advent of Christianity they were accordingly adapted—the ancient gods being replaced by Christ or one of His apostles. The colourful Kocevje legend runs as follows: On Christmas night Wotan on a white horse, with his followers and his dogs, rides through the woods, harried by devils. From the red-and-white foam flecks which fall to the ground from

8a. OAKHARE. *Polyp'ilus frondo'sus* (Dicks. ex Fr.) P. Karst., syn. *Polyp'orus frondo'sus* Dicks. ex Fr.

This Pore fungus, which may reach a width of between 12 and 20 inches, is composed of many patches and grows sparsely at the foot of old broad-leaved trees, oaks in particular. The Oakhare has a short, thick trunk, branching out continually. The thin, tough, ashy to grey-brown cap grows at the end of each stem and is semicircular to spatula-shaped. It is fibrous-striped, has a wavy or indented edge, and is provided with a short stalk growing sideways. The white to greyish tubes run down the stem and do not turn black when pressure is applied. Confusion is possible with the larger Giant Fungus (*Polypilus giganteus* [Pers. ex Fr.] Donk., syn. *Polyporus giganteus* Pers. ex Fr., to which it is closely related. The latter, however, has broader, bigger, but fewer caps, which are browner. Furthermore, the caps have pronounced belts and irregularly waved edges, and the pale pores become black when pressure is applied. This species is especially to be found at the foot of beeches. Both fungi are dangerous parasites with regard to trees.

8b. FAIRY-STOOL. *Cori'olus versicol'or* (L. ex Fr.) Quel., syn. *Polyp'orus versicol'or* L. ex Fr.

The Fairy-stool is certainly one of the most common and best-known toadstools. This graceful little lignicolous fungus is rarely found on conifers, but frequently on trunks, stumps, twigs, and even dressed wood of broad-leaved trees during the greater part of the year. The tough, leathery, thin-edged cap is about ¼ inch broad, fan-shaped to semicircular, and is attached to the wood by a fairly broad base. It grows mostly in tile-like or rosette-shaped groups. The glossy cap is silky and hairy in texture and concentrically zoned with various colours, which may be white to yellowish, ochre, grey to ashy, brownish and blue-black. The closer to the edge, the lighter the colour will be. The pores in the undersurface are white at first, later turning brownish.

This common fungus may be mistaken for the Ordinary Gill Woodfungus (*Lenzi'tes betuli'na* [L. ex Fr.] Fr.), which has roughly the same pattern and zoned cap. A marked difference, however, is the absence of the pores in the Gill Woodfungus species (having gills instead), and it usually grows on birch stumps.

8c. SULPHUR FUNGUS. *Laetiporus sulphu'reus* (Bull. ex Fr.) Murr., syn. *Tyromy'ces sulphu'reus* (Bull. ex Fr.) Donk., *Polyp'orus sulphu'reus* Bull. ex Fr.

This beautiful, striking Pore fungus, growing on broad-leaved trees, is fairly easy to identify. The stemless Sulphur Fungus usually appears in close groups above or alongside one another and may even grow together.

The colour of the upperside is sulphur-yellow to orange or even salmon pink, whereas the underside is sulphur-yellow and has tiny pores. The fruit-body may exceed 12 inches in breadth. This annual parasite is quite common and can be found from early summer until well into autumn. This fungus is unlikely to be confused with other species and grows high up in trees or on trunks of willows, poplars, beeches, and oaks.

his horse the Fly Agaric, with its red cap flecked with white, grows the next year. This legend reminds one of Christmas cards on which houses and snowy landscapes often include the Fly Agaric. The explanation might be twofold: Either the designer needed some red touches to brighten up the design, or else he might have had some knowledge of this legend.

In Silesia there is a legend about the well-known spring mushroom, the Morel (*Morchella esculenta*): The devil was in a bad temper when one day he met a wrinkled old woman in a wood. He seized her and cut her up into pieces, then strewed the pieces around the wood. Wherever a piece fell, there grew a morel—which, with a little imagination, can be thought of as wrinkled. For this reason an old woman is, in Silesia, called a "morchel." (Plate 30a.) The Hart Truffle (*Elaphomyces granulatus*) is said to have orginated from the spittle of witches and sorceresses, and Salomon-Voss quotes the popular name of these as "Hexenpizet" or Witches' Saliva. Another version is that its origin was the seed of the rutting hart (deer).

FAIRY RINGS

Fungus spawn grows out in every direction, as we shall see, and the fruit-bodies appear at its growing margin. This process may be studied with all kinds of ground fungi. When several specimens are found together it is worth looking to see whether they form part of a fairy ring.

In earlier times these fairy rings were well known, but owing to the veil of secrecy surrounding them and their rapid growth, they were looked upon suspiciously. At that time mushrooms were called "devil's bread, devil's food, brood of adders, children of darkness" and other such names. So a circle of these mysterious fungi discovered in the middle of a meadow or in a wood must have awakened people's imaginations; what was simpler than to connect them with the devil, witches, or fairies? It was thought that the fairies had danced there during the night and that toadstools appeared wherever their feet touched the ground. In some countries witches were substituted for fairies.

The French name for them is *rond de sorcières;* the German, *Hexenring;* in England and America they are known as "fairy rings."

Rather than go too deeply into these legends, we cite an example we have been following for a number of years. Dr Jacob P. Thijsse, one of the best Dutch popularisers of natural history, described the growth of such a ring in the years 1909 to 1911 and made a sketch of it. On November 7, 1909, he found a circle of the Great Violet Rider (*Lepista* [*Tricholoma*] *nuda*) measuring 94.5 by 74.8 inches with 24 specimens. In the following year, on November 4, 1910, the ring had grown to

9. BEAUTY STEM MYCENA. *Myce'na inclina'ta* (Fr.) Quel.

This species is one of the most beautiful lignicolous Mycenas. It grows in groups on old stumps, especially those of oaks, and is remarkable for the notched edge of the cap in its early stage. This species may be confused with the Helmet Mycena and the Striped Stalk Mycena, but differs from them by its ruddy-coloured stalk and its odour, resembling that of rancid fat. The striped cone- to bell-shaped cap is greyish brown to deep auburn. The close-growing gills are whitish. The smooth and crowned stalk, about 2½ to 3½ inches long, is whitish at first but soon turns auburn, beginning from the bottom, and the root-shaped foot has a velvety-haired surface. The species can be found in autumn.

154.3 by 144.4 inches with 153 specimens. On November 1, 1911, he counted 232 specimens; the diameter of the ring was now 218.2 by 208 inches. The drawing below clearly shows the development; it is also possible to see that normal growth has been interrupted by an obstacle. The mycelium was hindered by trying to grow on spruce leaves instead of the humus of loose oak leaves. The mycelium can be arrested or thwarted in its normal growth—in every direction— by many circumstances, such as a dry spot, a tree, or some other obstacle.

It is obvious from the dates mentioned that the Great Violet Rider appears in the late autumn. Many species form these fairy rings. An easy one to find is *Marasmius oreades*, the Fairy-ring Champignon, on meadows, grassy plots, lawns, and borders. (For a description, see page 85).

Scientific observers have attempted to understand the formation of the fairy ring, and a complete answer is still being sought; all kinds of factors—physiological, chemical, and biotic— seem to have a part to play. One short explanation is that all foodstuff is directed to the edge of the mycelium, where the fruit-bodies appear in a ring. It would become too involved at this point to become more specific. It is interesting to notice that in the case of the Fairy-ring Champignon a ring of dry grass may be seen on the inner side of the most recently formed mycelium. Just behind this, near the middle, the grass is again normal or even thicker than usual. As is often the case, it is easier to state this fact than to supply a satisfactory explanation.

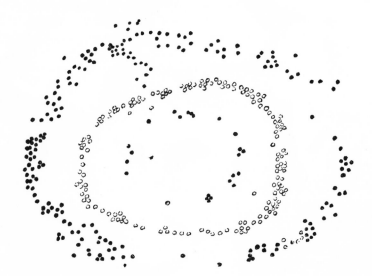

10a. BIRCHFUNGUS. *Pipto'porus betuli'nus* (Bull. ex Fr.) P. Karst., syn. *Polyp'orus betuli'nus* Bull ex Fr.

The Birchfungus has three peculiar features which make it easy to identify: it grows exclusively on trunks of old and diseased birches; its more or less kidney-shaped cap; and the existence of pores in the under-surface of the cap. The semicircular to kidney-shaped cap stands away from the trunk and grows on a very short stem if any. The cushion-like top is bare and smooth and has a colour that varies from grey to greyish brown. The pores are white, just like the flesh, which is soft and tenacious at first but later becomes corky in texture. At the top left-hand side of the picture a young specimen with its cap still knotty and tongue-shaped may be seen. The full-grown fungus has a cap up to 8 inches broad.

10b. SULPHUR MILK CAP. *Lacta'rius chrysorhe'us* Fr.

The name Sulphur Milk Cap indicates the exudation of very pungent milk when the mushroom is bruised or cut. This fluid is at first white but soon turns yellow. The cap, with a depression in the middle, is between 1¼ and 3 inches broad. The colour is orange to yellowish flesh-tinted with zoned darker markings or stains. The cream-coloured to pale ochre gills stand close together and run a little way down the stem. The stem is about 2½ inches long and somewhat paler than the cap. The Sulphur Milk Cap appears in summer and autumn and usually grows under oaks, thus making it easy to find.

10c. WOOLLY MILK CAP. *Lacta'rius tormino'sus* (Schaeff. ex Fr.) S. F. Gray.

This species generally appears under birches. The cap, 1¼ to 4 inches broad, is somewhat felty in texture and has an ochre to yellowish-pink colour with concentrically zoned dark markings and a depression in the middle. The inrolled margin is covered with whitish rugged, woolly hair (especially in the young fungi), and the older the fungus, the more difficult this is to see. The gills are pale rose to yellowish pink and run a little way down the stem. The hollow stem is about 2½ inches long, and the colour is almost identical with that of the cap. The colour-fast white milk is very acrid in taste.

This species still has a reputation for being poisonous and is often confused with the delicious Saffron Milk Cap (*Lacta'rius delicio'sus* [L. ex Fr.] S. F. Gray). This latter species also has a zoned cap of about the same colour but with no woolly margin. The sweet milk is saffron-coloured, and the various parts of this mushroom become greenish-stained when bruised or squeezed. The Saffron Milk Cap grows under conifers.

THE STRUCTURE AND LIFE OF FUNGI

What we see of a fungus is generally only a small part of the whole plant, the part which produces spores and which is called the fruit-body. This is misleading, since the name has nothing to do with fruit as such, nor can the spores be compared to seeds. As a rule, the spore consists of one cell only. Beginning with the fruit-body, the cycle proceeds as follows: The fruit-body produces spores in a spot favourable to germination, and these in turn produce threads, called hyphae. The hyphae develop into mycelium, or "spawn." From this spawn the mushroom or toadstool as we know it eventually grows, provided circumstances are favourable.

Before going into greater detail, let us consider the place of fungi among organisms. If they are considered as plants they are often grouped with bacteria, seaweeds, and lichens. Many believe, however, that fungi differ so profoundly in their structure and chemistry from all other organisms that they should be grouped in a separate category: a fungus kingdom comparable with the vegetable and animal kingdoms. Under the heading "fungi" are grouped "higher" and "lower" kinds. The "higher" kinds are mushrooms and toadstools, the "lower" are moulds. Their distinction from other plants lies in the fact that they have no chlorophyll, unlike green plants, which, by means of chlorophyll and light, build material for growth from carbonic acid, water, and some inorganic matter. Fungi, on the other hand, are almost entirely dependent on organic matter from other plants and animals for their development.

Fungi can "earn their living" in one of two ways. A mushroom or a mould must, like any other organism, obtain food by some means, not only for growth and preservation, but also to assure the continuation of its particular kind—in this case by the formation of spores. It can live off the dead matter of plants and animals, such as fallen leaves, small branches, compost, feathers, and fur. When fungi make use of such waste matter, they are called saprophytes; if, however, they feed on a living organism, be it plant or animal, they are parasites. Some fungi can be one or the other, according to conditions. The matter which they need is derived by a system of digests from the food material and compounded in a manner best suited to their growth. In an altered form this same matter returns to the earth when they decay.

This shows the important role fungi play in the economy of nature. They clear up all kinds of waste matter, transform it, and eventually make it available for the growth of other plants. Were this not the case, much matter would be taken out of the ground and not returned, to the detriment of the development of green plants. For the green plant is the beginning and the end of all life: this clearing up and transformation of varied matter occurs not only with the well-known wood and field toadstool, but just as much with the moulds in the ground that we, on

11a. PORCELAIN FUNGUS. *Oudemansiel' la mu' cida* (Schrad. ex Fr.) Höhn., syn. *Muci' dula mu' ci-da* (Schrad. ex Fr.) Pat.

This species possesses striking features and is consequently easy to recognise when one is out looking for fungi. Identification is facilitated by the knowledge that the Porcelain Fungus usually grows on diseased or dead beeches or their fallen branches. Such a tree or part of a tree is very often completely studded with fruit-bodies. The whole fungus—especially the cap in wet weather—is glistening white and slimy to the touch but turns grey to greyish brown later. The vaulted cap is 3¼ inches in diameter, thin-fleshed and translucent. The gills are wide apart. The fairly long, bent stalk has a striped ring.

This graceful parasite fungus can be found from late summer to late autumn on the above-mentioned host.

11b. LITTLE CLUSTER FUNGUS. *Kuehneromy' ces muta' bilis* (Schaeff. ex Fr.) Sing. & Smith, syn. *Pholio' ta muta' bilis* (Schaeff. ex Fr.) Kummer.

This fungus has a very hygrophanous cap which changes its colour according to humidity conditions; this fact is indicated by the Latin specific name *mutabilis* —changeable.

The Little Cluster Fungus generally grows in bundles on stumps and roots of deciduous trees, rarely conifers, and can be found from early summer until late autumn.

The cap—1½ to 3¼ inches—is at first semi-spherical in shape but later flattens out, though a slight protrusion remains in the centre. In a moist atmosphere the colour of the cap is dark cinnamon to auburn, otherwise paler, even yellowish brown; the edge is the last part of the cap to assume the lighter colour. These differences can be easily distinguished in the picture. The cap looks and feels greasy, especially in damp surroundings. The gills grow closely together and run a little way down the stem. Pale brown at first, they later turn rust-coloured. The thin stalk is usually bent and up to 3¼ inches long, provided with a brown ring. Below this ring the stalk is rust-coloured with dark, outstanding scales; higher up, the surface is lighter and smooth to the touch. The special ring mark may disappear when the fungus ages.

Without its stem, the Little Cluster Fungus makes excellent eating. Do not confuse this species with the Honey Fungus or Sulphur Tuft, which is described elsewhere in this book.

11c. YELLOW CORAL FUNGUS. *Rama' ria fla' va* (Fr.) Quel., syn. *Clava' ria fla' va* Fr.

The light yellow to sulphur-coloured branches grow in a fist-sized cluster from a short whitish trunk. The numerous forked, erect stems have stumpy bipartite extremities.

This beautiful Coral Fungus can be found in deciduous forests (beeches) and pinewoods in the summer and autumn.

The closely related Golden Coral Fungus (*Rama' ria au' rea* [Schaeff. ex Fr.] Quel., syn. *Clava' ria au' rea* Schaeff. ex Fr.) has golden to orange branches with forked endings. This species is easily mistaken for the Yellow Coral Fungus and often proves a poser for authorities on fungi. The sturdier Beautiful Coral Fungus (*Rama' ria formo' sa* [Pers. ex Fr.] Quel., syn. *Clava' ria formo' sa* Pers. ex Fr.) sprouts from a well-developed white trunk and has rosy to flesh-coloured branches with yellowish sprigs at the ends (tricoloured). The white flesh tastes bitter and is highly purgative. Consequently, this species is considered to be poisonous, in contrast to the two first-mentioned varieties.

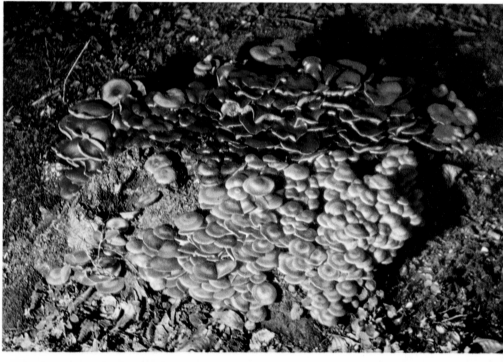

our walks through the countryside, never see because they are such tiny threads. Yet a similar phenomenon may be seen at home in the mildew on stale bread, where much the same action is taking place. Fungi play the major role in this particular way, but many other organisms, such as ground bacteria, worms, wood lice, and similar insects, also contribute to the disposal of rubbish.

No consideration—and this is deliberate—has been given here to the gathering of fungi for purposes of consumption, for because of over-intensive picking, particularly in the neighbourhood of large towns, the most favoured edible varieties have become scarce.

Fungi fall into four large groups based on microscopic observation as to how the spores are formed. For our purposes only two of the groups are important, the second and third in the following divisions:

PHYCOMYCETES

These are unicellular or thread-like but mostly without cross walls. The spores are produced in indefinite numbers in sporangia. Although the name Phycomycetes may sound strange to us, we are in fact familiar with many representatives of this group. Instances are: the universally feared potato-blight (*Phytophthora infestans*), mildew on stale bread, and the mould which coats flies in the autumn with what appears to be a white down (*Empusa muscae*); the fly eventually dies, since the threads of mould consume its body. These threads work outwards to form spores that have the white powder-like appearance on the fly's body. There are also the water moulds that can attack wounded fish—a nuisance to aquaria owners; these moulds are species of *Saprolegnia* and *Achlya*.

ASCOMYCETES

These consist of threads with cross walls and are complete with fruit-body. The spores are produced in a definite number—mostly eight in a cell, called a sac or ascus. The spores are thus formed inside a cell. In this group, Ascomycetes or Sac fungi, a large number of the species have fruit-bodies only a millimetre or two long, although some larger kinds also occur. To this same group belong the Morel, the White Morsel fungus, and the Great Orange Elf-cup fungus. (See Plates 30a, 31c, 32a.)

The Ascomycetes are subdivided into the Discomycetes (Cup fungi) and the Pyrenomycetes (Flask fungi).

It is characteristic of the Discomycetes, to which the Great Orange Cup belongs, that the spores in the microscopic asci on the inner side of the cup—called apothecium (2)—are formed as a hymenium or fertile layer. In the Pyrenomycetes fewer asci sit in a simple flask-shaped organ called a perithecium (1). There may be many perithecia in one fruit-body. To these fungi

12. FLAT TINDERFUNGUS. *Ganoder'ma applana'tum* (Pers. ex Wallr.) Pat., syn. *Polyp'orus applana'tus* Pers. ex Wallr.

As this species gets a fresh layer of tubes each year of its life, the Flat Tinderfungus may survive for many years. It can be found on various broad-leaved trees, often in overlapping groups. The flattened fruit-body, between 4 and 10 inches broad, is semicircular to console-shaped and grows without a stem from a trunk or stump.

The upperside, ocherous at first, may be covered with brown powder later on. The surface is rather lumpy and has concentrically running grooves.

New layers of tubes are white and curled back at the edge, and these account for the light-coloured margin.

The whitish pores turn brown when pressure is applied or when the fungus is aging.

belong, for example, the Candle-snuff (*Xylaria hypoxylon*), and the Wood Club Fungus (*Xylaria polymorpha*). (See Plates 14a-b.) For the purpose of close examination of the perithecium it is best to select the second-named kind, the Wood Club Fungus. Upon cutting this fungus in half, the perithecia are seen just under the surface and should be examined under a magnifying glass. The Wood Club Fungus may be described as follows: very variable in form, size, and thickness; may be up to 4 inches high. It may assume the form of a knob, a hand, a bullet, or a bobbin. It is black outside, white inside. The Wood Club Fungus has a tough wood-like substance and is to be found during the whole year on rotting wood and stumps. It is frequently seen on the ground, though not always easily discovered owing to its black colour.

The perithecium can also be found in the more common Candle-snuff, although here it is not so prominent.

BASIDIOMYCETES

The spores are produced in a definite number, mostly four, on sterigmata, or stalks, on microscopic cells called basidia. To this group belong the Gill, the Pore, and the Paunch fungi. Examples of these are: the Fly Agaric, the Squirrel's Bread, the various *Polyporus* species, the Earth-stars, and the Stinkhorn, Figure 1, page 61 (3, 4, 5).

DEUTEROMYCETES

The spores, called in this case conidia, occur directly on threads or in very small fruit-bodies. To this group, also known as *Fungi Imperfecti*, belong a heterogeneous collection of moulds, including one which has become famous—namely, *Penicillium notatum*. This mould, discovered by Sir Alexander Fleming, to be the source of penicillin, has already saved countless lives. Another well-known mould of this order is the green mould on cheese.

It is difficult for a layman to determine without a microscope the group to which a fungus belongs. As typical of the Sac fungi let us select the Great Orange Cup (Plate 32a), and of the Gill fungi group, the well-known Fly Agaric (Plate 20).

For the sake of clarity, the diagram on p. 61 shows an ascus with spores of an Ascomycete, and also of a Basidiomycete with basidia.

In the drawing of the fungus the asci are reproduced in enlargement. With them are other cells, empty of spores, called paraphyses. In the various species of ascus-bearing fungi great differences exist in the form and the markings of the ascospores, which can be observed only under the microscope. The classification of the smaller kinds is achieved largely by observing

13a. SCALY CLUSTER FUNGUS. *Pholio'ta squarro'sa* (Müll. ex Fr.) Kummer.

The Scaly Cluster Fungus, also called the Scaly Pholiota, is a parasitic wood fungus, growing in autumn in clusters at the feet of all kinds of broad-leaved trees or on their roots.

The entire toadstool, both cap and stem, is yellow to yellow-brown and well covered with numerous brown, coarse, recurved scales, which often disappear in rain or with age. The tough stem, usually curved and 3¼ to 4 inches long, has a disappearing ring; above the ring the stem is smooth. The cap is at first convex but flattens out with age and may become between 4 and 4¾ inches wide. The gills are crowded close together and are olive-yellow, turning to brown. The recurved brown scales on a lighter background and the fact that these fungi grow in clusters are distinct features. It is sometimes confused with the Honey Fungus (*Armilla'ria mel'lea* [Vahl. ex Fr.] Kummer) (page 98), which is lignicolous and also grows in clusters. The spores of the Honey Fungus, however, are white, whereas those of the Scaly Cluster Fungus are brown.

13b. GREY STRIA CAP. *Copri'nus dissemina'tus* (Pers. ex Fr.) S. F. Gray, syn. *Psathyrel'la dissemina'ta* (Pers. ex Fr.) Quel.

The name Grey Stria Cap clearly describes this small, fragile toadstool. It is grey to grey-brown, bell-shaped and striated, and grows in enormous numbers crowded together, often hundreds at a time. The striated cap, about ½ inch, is ovoid to bell-shaped; it is yellowish white when young, turning grey with a light ochre top as it grows older. The gills are at first whitish, then turn greyish to ash-black and do not merge. The stem has a maximum length of 2 inches. The Grey Stria Caps are delicate and perishable. They are to be found from spring until autumn seemingly sown at the feet of trees, on stumps of broad-leaved trees, and on decaying wood.

13c. FAN. *Schizophy'llum commu'ne* Fr.

This toadstool is particularly interesting because of its peculiar gills. Before examining the gill structure we give first a short description of the species. It is shell- to fan-shaped, growing on wood on a narrowed base. The thin, tough cap—up to 1¼ inches—has an inrolled edge and is greyish white to brownish grey on top; felty or woolly in texture.

The gills or ridges are ashy to grey-purple and split along the edges. As a rule, the Fan grows edge overlapping edge on cut or dying trunks, especially those of broad-leaved trees, and can be found practically throughout the year.

The peculiar gills, partly split and hygroscopic, curl back in dry weather and unroll in damp weather. Some suppose that this protects the spore-producing surface from excessive drying out in dry weather. Spores escape only when the half-gills are unrolled.

13d. INDIGO BOLETUS. *Gyro'porus cyane'scens* (Bull. ex Fr.) Quel., syn. *Bole'tus cyane'scens* Bull. ex Fr.

This tube fungus is entirely yellow-white to fawn-coloured. The lumpy surface of the vaulted cap—up to 5¼ inches—and the stem—up to 2¾ inches—which is thickened down towards the base, are both somewhat felty in texture. The underside of the cap, with crowded pores, is whitish to light ochre at first, turning rather yellow later. At ruptures or bruising, the flesh turns a beautiful indigo to cornflower blue, which later fades. This bolete is found in sandy deciduous forests and pinewoods, but because of its precarious existence is rarely found. The blue discolouring of the flesh has nothing to do with whether the fungus is edible or not. This species is in fact a very good eating fungus. No other bolete turns such a deep blue as the Indigo Boletus. The photograph shows this species growing on the slope of a recently cut trench—one reason that the stem does not show up clearly.

paraphyses, asci, and spores. Whenever the spores are ripe—they are called ascospores—the sap pressure in the little sac forces them out. If many sacs discharge their spores simultaneously, a cloud of spores over the fruit-body will be seen. This phenomenon can be produced out of doors or at home—if circumstances are favourable—by giving the fruit-body a gentle tap.

The group Basidiomycetes includes fungi in which the spores are formed on lamellae or gills. The spores, when ripe, are shot off the sterigmata, fall down between the gills, and, as with the Sac fungi, are blown away by the lightest air current.

Similar to the Ascomycetes, cells sometimes occur in which no spores are formed; these are then called cystidia, varying greatly in form according to their kind. The basidia and cystidia together form the hymenium of the Basidiomycetes.

It is interesting to prove that the spores fall between the lamellae. This may be done by the following experiment: Cut the stalk off a gilled mushroom close to the cap and place the cap on a glass plate to stand overnight, preferably with a glass cover over the top so that the spores may drop without danger of their being blown away. Provided a ripe specimen has been chosen, a regular pattern will be formed on the glass plate by the fallen spores; where the gills have rested on the glass there will be no spores. The colour of the spores vary according to the kind of toadstool. A white or black piece of paper under the glass will make these easier to see, and a fixative, such as used by painters, will preserve the pattern.

In nature the spores are spread around by currents of air so that they cannot come to rest directly under the toadstool. In some cases however, where toadstools grow in clusters, the spores may fall on to the cap of another specimen. This occurs with the Honey Fungus (*Armillaria mellea*) and the Oyster Cap (*Pleurotus ostreatus*). Owing to Elias Fries' observation of the different colours of the spores, he came to classify fungi into various families and genera; for spores may be white, yellowish, pink, brown, or purple to black. A microscope, even of low magnification, will enable an observer to appreciate their colour, form, and ornamentation. The form of spores

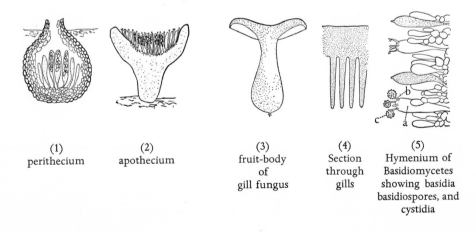

(1)	(2)	(3)	(4)	(5)
perithecium	apothecium	fruit-body of gill fungus	Section through gills	Hymenium of Basidiomycetes showing basidia basidiospores, and cystidia

14a. WOOD CLUB FUNGUS. *Xyla'ria polymor'pha* (Pers. ex Fr.) Grev.

This variety of the Flask fungi (Pyrenomycetes) is covered with small warts and has a brown-black to black colour but a white interior. The Latin specific name indicates that this fungus may grow in various shapes: it may be club-shaped, hand-shaped, finger-shaped, spindle-shaped or ovoid.

This corky, sometimes rather woody species may be up to 4 inches tall and 1¼ inches wide and is often forked and forms a thin stem near the foot.

It generally grows in large groups on stumps or on mouldered wood; sometimes it appears to grow on the ground, but in fact some wood will be found hidden under the surface. To verify that the Wood Club Fungus belongs to the Flask fungi, we must cut it lengthwise. With the assistance of a magnifying glass we see the submerged urns or perithecia at the sides, where spores are formed in little sacs.

This common species can be found practically throughout the year, but because of its dark colour it may often easily be overlooked. Confusion with any other species is seldom possible.

14b. CANDLE-SNUFF FUNGUS. *Xyla'ria hypox'ylon* (L. ex Fr.) Grev.

This species belongs to the Flask fungi (Pyrenomycetes) and is especially characterised by its shape and the black and white colour. The Candle-snuff Fungus is lignicolous, very common on old stumps, dead and mouldered wood, and grows throughout the year. The fungus has a flattened, antler-like structure of a tough and cork-like consistency; the lower part is black, felty, and thinned down to a kind of stalk.

Spores are formed in little urns or perithecia, which can be seen near the edge through a magnifying glass when the fungus is cut lengthwise. A type of spore—conidium—is formed when the specimen is young, and this accounts for the white coating on the top. When aging, this wood fungus is completely black and rather warty to the touch.

14c. PURPLE KNOT FUNGUS. *Cory'ne sarcoi'des* (Jacq. ex Fr.) Tul.

This Sac fungus (Ascomycetes) is often mistaken for a Quivering Fungus because of its jelly-like appearance and the fact that it grows on wood. A microscopic examination, however, will give a decisive answer.

The species is commonly found on stumps and decayed wood—especially on beeches—and has a reddish-violet to deep purple colour which is intensified by the degree of humidity. The Purple Knot Fungus usually grows in clusters and is jelly-like and toughly gelatinous. When young (see photo) this fungus has a brain-like structure which turns cup-shaped later and will then be about ¼ inch wide.

may be round, angular, oval, or elongated, with or without spots, warts, or markings. In the case of *Russula* an attempt has been made to classify species on the grounds of the ornamentation on the spores.

Let us consider further the spores and the sprouting hypha or thread which grows into a mycelium. When the spore has left the fruit-body, much depends on the spot where it falls as to whether an hypha will sprout. A spore makes certain demands, like the seed of any green plant, requiring dampness, warmth, and the substratum it needs for development. When all circumstances are favourable, these threads branch out and form the mycelium. This mycelium or spawn—a mass of hyphae—is the vegetative part of the fungus. For it must extract from the ground, or from the substratum on which it grows, the foodstuffs necessary for the building of the fruit-body that will in due time be responsible for the formation of spores. The spawn therefore must also be considered as a feeding machine.

Always taking into account circumstances, the spawn grows, from its beginning, in all directions. The time of year is important, particularly so far as damp and warmth are concerned. Although the majority of toadstools appear in late summer and autumn, there are certain kinds which may be found the year round, and there are also certain spring fungi. Well-known examples are the Morel (*Morchella*) and the Spring Rider (*Calocybe [Tricholoma] georgii*), which may be found on grassy spots in May and June. The Spring Rider has a cream-coloured cap—up to 4 inches—with the beginnings of a rolled-in edge, widely spaced off-white gills and stalk. Its flesh has a farinaceous smell. Some, however, do not attain full growth until late summer or winter. Another common variety is the Velvet Foot or Winter Fungus (*Flammulina [Collybia] velutipes*). This is easily recognised, as its name—Velvet Foot—draws attention to its velvety dark brown stalk. The fungus grows in clusters on stumps or tree trunks and has yellowish gills fairly widely spaced. The Fir Slimy-Cap (*Hygrophorus [Limacium] hypothejus*), which also appears late in the year, grows only in coniferous woods, and the surface of the cap is waxy. The colour of the cap is olive-brown or yellowish. The broad, separate yellowish gills slope from the stalk. It generally appears when the first night frosts may be expected—around November.

Since many varieties of fungi appear as early as July and continue throughout the autumn, it is evident that mycology can be studied during much of the year; but it is also true to say that the majority are to be found in autumn.

After the mycelium is well established, it begins to form fruit-bodies. At the edges of the developed spawn small knobs appear that will grow into toadstools, and generally these are to be found above ground. In the case of truffles, false truffles, and the like, the fruit-bodies remain more or less below ground.

It is not difficult to find spawn if one wanders through the woods in autumn: search for a

15a. PURPLE BLEWIT. *Tricholomop'sis ru'tilans* (Schaeff. ex Fr.) Sing., syn. *Tricholo'ma ru'tilans* (Schaeff. ex Fr.) Kummer.

This species is quite common on trunks and stumps of conifers and is easy to recognise because the upperside of the cap is covered with felty fibrils or scales on a yellow background. This yellow shows clearly at the edges of old specimens. The underside of the cap has golden gills. The cap is bell-shaped at first but widens later on, up to 4 inches.

The yellow stalk, up to 4¾ inches in length, is covered with purple fibrils like the cap, though to a lesser degree. The flesh of both cap and stalk is yellow.

The Purple Blewit grows either individually or in groups from July to November and is unlikely to be mistaken for any other kind of fungus.

15b. RUSTSPOT FUNGUS or SPOTTED COLLYBIA. *Collyb'ia macula'ta* (Alb. & Schw. ex Fr.) Kummer.

This species can be considered as the biggest in the genus *Collybia* and is also conspicious for its white colour. The cap, gills, and stalk are usually covered with rust-coloured spots, later turning brown, and thus accounting for its name: Rustspot Fungus.

The cap may be as wide as 4¾ inches and is bare and fleshy. Though at first spherical with an inrolled edge, it later becomes flatter and wavy. The gills stand close to each other and change their colour from whitish to yellowish. The cartilaginous white stalk, up to 4¾ inches in length, is striped and cylindrical to spindle-shaped, tapering at the bottom. When aging, the whole fungus turns brown. This *Collybia* is very common and usually grows in rings or groups.

It can be found from summer until late autumn, especially in pinewoods.

The flesh tastes bitter, and the fungus is quite unpalatable.

15c. TOPFUNGUS. *Polysti'ctus peren'nis* (L. ex Fr.) P. Karst., syn. *Polyp'orus peren'nis* L. ex Fr.

This beautiful Pore fungus, concentrically ringed and more or less funnel-shaped, is one of the few Polyporaceae that grow on the ground instead of on wood. The short stem of the majority of this genus grows from the side and not from the centre (or it may be nonexistent). The Topfungus, however, usually has a short central stem. The cap is round, thin, fleshy, and leathery; the colour of the rings varies from yellow-brown to auburn. The width of the cap may reach 4 inches, and very often the caps of some specimens are found to have grown together; this may also happen with the stems.

The angular pores in the undersurface of the cap run a little way down the stem; the colour turns from whitish to brownish as the fungus ages. This top-like annual fungus generally grows on sandy soil in pinewoods from summer until very late autumn. Because of the tough, leathery composition, the species is easily dried.

fungus growing on decayed leaves. The white threads will be found mostly among the leaves. Having seen various kinds of mycelia, one soon reaches the conclusion that there is little difference among them. The few exceptions are violet or yellow spawns. Though the differences in the form and colour of the fruit-body are great, the appearance of the spawn remains uniform. It is therefore impossible to determine a fungus from the mycelium. Apart from the colour, there are relatively few differences to be observed: some mycelia have grown to thick strands— about a millimetre thick—that are sometimes white or range from dark brown to black. These thick strands, or cords, are called rhizomorphs. The cords are easily seen in the Stinkhorn; this fungus is easy to find, since its carrion-like smell will lead the way. Carefully uproot the fungus, and the white cords will appear. With a little luck one may possibly find at the same time an emerging fungus. The not yet fully grown Stinkhorn is enclosed in a kind of egg: in the larger variety it is the size of a hen's egg, in the smaller the size of a pigeon's egg.

A dark mycelium cord is best seen in the Honey Fungus (*Armillaria mellea*). This fungus may be found at the foot of a tree, and the black cords—like shoe laces—lie beneath the bark. Another easily observed variety of mycelium is a firm, frequently rounded mass of hyphae called sclerotium. Sclerotia are generally contained in the smaller species of fungi, such as the Ochre Tuber (*Microcollybia* [*Collybia*] *cirrhata*).

To the group of fungi with stems belong not only the Gill fungi but also quite a large number which produce no gills, bearing their spores otherwise. In order to avoid complication we shall only give a broad outline. Further details should be sought in the literature available.

Our classification therefore is as follows:

HYMENOMYCETES
  Agaricales
    Agaricaceae (1)   Gill fungi
    Boletaceae (2)
  Aphyllophorales
    Polyporaceae (3)
    Hydnaceae (4)   Spine fungi
    Clavariaceae (5)   Club or Coral fungi
    Thelephoraceae (6)   Crust fungi
    (*inclusive of*
    Corticiaceae)
    Tremellales (7)   Quivering fungi
  GASTEROMYCETES (8)   PAUNCH FUNGI

16a. YELLOW RING BOLETUS or ELEGANT BOLETUS. *Su'illus grevil'leii* (Klotsch) Sing., syn. *Bole'tus e'legans* Schum. ex Fr.

This bolete is not hard to find if you look in the vicinity of larch trees. It is associated with this one kind of tree. Whenever the weather is not too unfavourable, the larch toadstool, as it is also called, can be found. Identification poses few problems, since the whole plant is yellow. As with all other kinds of boletes, its underside is formed of tiny tubes. The fleshy cap, up to 4¾ inches in diameter, is lemon-yellow to golden or golden brown and is at first spherical in shape, later opening out. It is slimy in damp weather. The pores on the underside of the cap are yellow. In their young state they are covered with a membrane that, with growth, tears loose from the rim of the cap and remains as a ring around the stalk. The stalk and the flesh of the cap are also yellow. Confusion is possible with the Milk Boletus (*Su'illus granula'tus* [L. ex Fr.] O.K.), which has no ring, a darker cap, and when young has droplets on the underside of the cap.

16b. BROWN RING BOLETUS. *Su'illus lu'teus* (L. ex Fr.) S. F. Gray, syn. *Bole'tus lu'teus* L. ex Fr.

This species also has a ring around the stalk, originating in the same way as that of the Yellow Ring Boletus, but this ring ranges from yellowish brown to purplish brown, according to age. The upper surface is yellow-brown, ruddy, or chocolate, often with violet tints. In damp weather it is very slimy. The fleshy cap is hemispherical when young, later spreading out to a diameter of 4 to 4¾ inches. The yellowish-white flesh of the cap does not discolour when exposed to the air. The underside of the cap is from lemon to olive in colour, and the pores are very small. The solid stalk, up to 3¼ inches long, is yellow above the ring and covered with whitish granules, later darkening.

The Brown Ring Boletus usually appears between June and November in pine forests and fields.

16c. CURLED-EDGE FUNGUS. *Paxil'lus involu'tus* (Batsch. ex Fr.) Fr.

This toadstool has a place all to itself among the "true" gilled fungi. This is because it has two peculiarities that link it with the boletes. The tubes of *Boletus* can be easily removed without damaging the flesh of the cap; this is also the case with the gills of *Paxillus;* they may be scraped off with a fingernail. The gills, moreover, extending part of the way down the stem, are to a certain extent united near the stem, thus also resembling the tubes of *Boletus.* Systematists therefore range this genus with the Boletaceae; it might thus be called a bolete with gills.

P. involutus is generally found in pinewoods and deciduous forests, fields, by roadsides, in gardens and parks, even on wood. It appears as early as June and can still be found in late autumn. It owes its name to the fact that in young specimens the margin of the cap is rolled under. The cap, 4 inches wide, ochre to olive-brown in colour, flattens out later and then becomes somewhat bowl-shaped. The decurrent, limp gills are closely set, lighter in colour than the surface of the cap, and become darker when pressed. The short stalk is about the same colour as the cap. The flesh smells and tastes rather sour.

Because of its peculiar structure, the Curled-edge Fungus is not easily confused with other species.

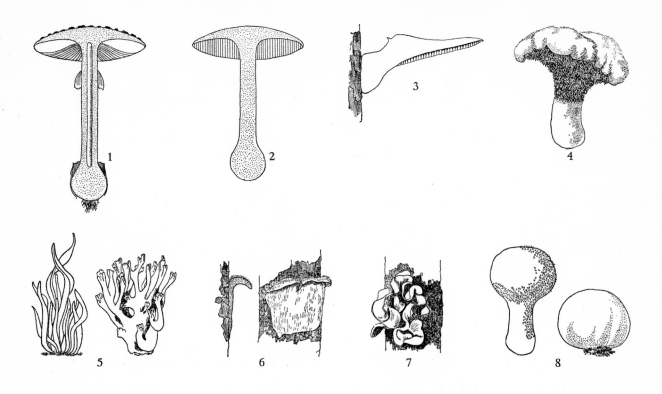

One or more species of each group is reproduced in this book. With the exception of the Paunch fungi—about which more later—all this group have one fact in common: The basidia are formed outside the fruit-body.

On our expeditions we are more likely to come across the Gill fungi than other varieties. It is important, therefore, to mention their most striking characteristics so that we may identify as many as possible in the field and may also be able to check them more easily with reference books. Only a very few, owing to their size, are easily distinguishable. Toadstools which produce brown spores (amongst which are the veiled fungi) are some of the most difficult to identify. When young, these veiled fungi may be recognised by the veil or cortina covering the mature gills. When the fungus develops, this veil is disrupted and parts of it may still be seen around the stem and sometimes on the edge of the cap. Most, if not all, of these brown-spored forms grow in the woods on the ground and never on the wood itself. Plates 3b, 3c will make it clear that many of them are coloured.

One of the easily identified varieties of Gill fungi is the Milk fungus (*Lactarius*). Its characteristic is the milky fluid that oozes out when any part is damaged or broken off. This milky juice may be watery, white, yellow, or orange; it can even change colour—as from white to yellow. The flesh of some varieties has a sharp taste, and one may have to taste it to differentiate

17a. FIRFOOT FUNGUS. *Hapalo'pilus schweinit'zii* (Fr.) Donk., syn. *Polyp'orus schweinit'zii* Fr.

This root parasite can be found at the feet of conifers or in close proximity to such trees; it hardly ever grows on the trunks. Sometimes the Firfoot Fungus may ostensibly seem to be growing on the ground, but one can soon see that in fact it is parasitising the roots of its host. The species is to be found from summer through to autumn, but is by no means common.

This is one of the few Polyporaceae with a more or less centrally growing stalk instead of a stalk growing sideways. The flat, tough, fleshy cap—10 or more inches in diameter—is a beautiful auburn with a bright golden margin, and it is covered with rough and felty hairs. The pores are greenish yellow. Specimens of this fungus often are to be found growing together.

17b. SCALED PRICKLE FUNGUS. *Sar'codon imbrica'tus* (L. ex Fr.) P. Karst., syn. *Hyd'num imbrica'tum* L. ex Fr.

This fungus is very scaled, with coarse dark-brown scales standing outwards and growing against a lighter background. The Prickle fungus is soon recognised, provided the underside is also examined; this will reveal the prickles, at first a dirty white but later turning brown. The greyish stalk is short, and the diameter of the cap is up to 8 inches.

The Scaled Prickle fungus can be found in sandy pinewoods, growing in large groups from summer to autumn.

This edible toadstool is also used to season soups and sauces.

17c. RESIN FUNGUS. *Penio'phora gigan'tea* (Fr.) Massee, syn. *Corti'cium gigan'tea* Fr.

The Resin Fungus is clearly a species of the Crust fungi (Corticiaceae), since this dull-coloured species spreads out like a crust on the wood on which it grows. Nonetheless, the white to greyish patches (somewhat like candle grease) on stumps, branches, or needles of coniferous trees in pinewoods are apt to lead the layman to mistake this species of Crust fungi for a resinous secretion of the conifer.

The picture speaks for itself. The thin and irregularly shaped crust may be 12 or more inches wide. The tenacious flesh is waxy to resinous in texture and pressed close to the wood. The surface may be smooth, but as a rule it will be found rather lumpy, quite often with serrated edges.

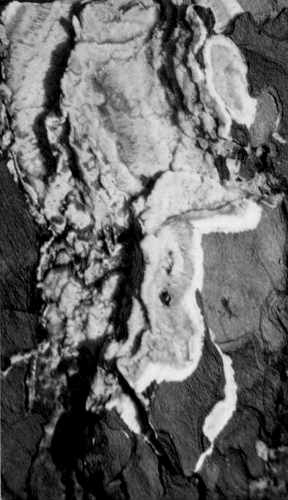

one kind from another: a light touch with the tip of the tongue may be made without danger. The colour of the fluid may also help identification. Most of these are toadstools with short stems and are all to be found in woods.

Closely related to the Milk fungi are the Russulas. Although without milky fluid, *Russula* has much in common with *Lactarius*. Both are genuine ground fungi. The gills of the Milk fungi may sometimes descend to the stem, but in *Russula* these remain at right angles to the stem, like the spokes of a wheel. Also characteristic of this variety is the flesh, particularly of the stem, which is very brittle and not fibrous. Many of the Russulas are brightly coloured: red, yellow, off-white, variegated purple, or green. This green has nothing in common with the green found in plants owing to chlorophyll, since mushrooms have none. The taste of fungi also varies: some are difficult to distinguish, since colours tend to disappear according to the age of the specimen or the amount of rain wash. If information other than form and spore marks is required, use must be made of chemical reagents. The flesh may react by changing colour. The spores may then become white or yellow to orange.

Another genus is *Amanita*, some of which are poisonous and deadly. The characteristics should therefore be carefully memorised. They are fairly large ground toadstools with white or light-coloured gills. The stem often has a ring or cuff. A specimen without a ring is the Grisette (*Amanita fulva*) (Plate 1c). Most of them also have a thickening at the base of the stem—a sort of pocket or sac, the volva. The cap is nearly always covered with spots or warts. These spots or warts are relics of a veil (*velus universale*) which covered the young fungus. On development, the veil is broken and patches remain—the number depending on the type—on the cap; the rest can be found round the edge and as a pocket at the base of the stem. In addition to this universal veil, the genus has a partial veil (*velum partiale*) protecting the gills (*lamellae*) in its early stage. The partial veil also occurs in some of the boletes, pressed close to the stem. Examples of this genus are the Yellow Ring Boletus and the Brown Ring Boletus (*Boletus luteus*) (Plates 16a-b).

The partial veil can be most easily seen between the edge of the cap and the stem on young specimens (Plate 16b, above right). During growth the veil parts company with the edge of the cap and remains as a cuff or ring around the stem. The best example to study is the Fly Agaric, beginning with the youngest specimens, which look like small boletes pushing up out of the ground. From the side, both the universal and partial veils will be seen. Sometimes the imprint of the gills is still noticeable on the ring. It is best to avoid eating any of the Amanitas—although some are edible—until they have been meticulously examined. Most cases of severe poisoning occur through eating this genus, for the green Death Cap (*Amanita phalloides*) and the Panther (*Amanita pantherina*) are often confused with edible mushrooms.

Another genus with a ring around the stem is the Parasol (*Lepiota*). In the larger specimens

18a. SPONGE FUNGUS. *Massee'ola cri'spa* (Wulf. ex Fr.) O.K., syn. *Sparas'sis cri'spa* (Wulf. ex Fr.) Fr.

The Sponge Fungus belongs to the genus of the Club and Coral fungi (Clavariaceae) and is confined to conifers, growing at the feet or on the roots.

The fruit-body, up to 12 inches wide, is the size of a cauliflower, spherical in shape and often somewhat flattened. The white to yellowish colour turns brown as the fungus ages. Peculiar to this species are the intertwining branches, frizzed at the ends, with a brittle, broad and flat leaf- to spatula-shaped structure.

The fungus grows on a short trunk and may weigh many pounds. This beautiful and interesting Coral fungus is common from late summer into late autumn.

18b. EARSPOON FUNGUS. *Auriscal'pium vulga're* (S. F. Gray), syn. *Hyd'num auriscal'pium* (L. ex Fr.

This little brown fungus does not show up clearly against the dark background in woods, but since the Earspoon Fungus grows only on old, fallen—and even buried— pine cones, it should not be difficult to trace a specimen. Since there are many kinds of fungi of various genera growing on pine cones, a description of this specific variety of the Prickle fungi will be helpful.

The cap, tough and hairy, is brown to brown-black, ¼ inch in diameter, and kidney-shaped. Depending on age, the prickles may vary from greyish white to brownish. The brown and sideways-growing stalk is 1¼ to 2¼ inches long and covered with hair.

The name *auriscalpium* (earspoon) stems from the resemblance of this fungus to an old-fashioned ear-spoon.

18c. FALSE TRUFFLE. *Rhizo'pogon lute'olus* Fr. ex Nordh.

To describe the False Truffle is not difficult; to find it in the fields, however, is by no means an easy task. It may be easily overlooked—mainly for three reasons: It grows only partly above the ground; the brownish colour is not very conspicuous; and, finally, it is very small.

The False Truffle belongs to the extensive group of Puffballs; namely, to the genus *Rhizopogon* of the line of False Truffles (Hymenogastraceae).

Notwithstanding some resemblance in appearance, this genus bears no relationship to the real Truffles. The latter species belong to the Sac fungi (Ascomycetes).

The fruit-body of the False Truffle is more or less globular to tuberiform, not broader than 2¼ inches, and partly covered by dark mycelial cords; the original dirty-white colour soon turns brownish yellow to olive-brown. When mature, the hard crust bursts open irregularly and later changes into an olive-green substance with an offensive smell.

The False Truffle grows in sandy, coniferous surroundings and can be found in autumn.

this ring can often be moved up or down the stem. It is formed in almost the same manner as in *Amanita* and is also the remains of the veil protecting the gills; the difference is that in *Lepiota* the ring abandons the stem before leaving the edge of the cap. Also different is the surface of the cap, which is scaly and flaky, not spotted. These Parasol scales are hard to remove, while the *Amanita* spots are easily rubbed off. The wide-open gills are white and not connected to the stem, and the stem is easily removed from the cap. In many cases the foot of the stem has thickened into a tuberous form, but without the sac or pocket that occurs in *Amanita*. The genus *Lepiota* produces some very large specimens: the Parasol can be 16 inches high and 12 inches across its cap. With the smaller varieties—and they can also be very small—there is little to recognise, even when the fruit-body is full grown, apart from the single ring. The spores are white. (Plate 26a-c).

Because of the great differences among members of the genus *Lepiota*, it has been subdivided into smaller genera. Thus the Parasol used to be called *Lepiota procera*, but in some of the present naming systems it is called *Macrolepiota procera*. Other genera have also been subdivided. The last word on the correct systematic classification of fungi has still to be said!

This is also true of the Blewits (*Tricholoma*). These more or less medium-to-large-sized toadstools are generally so compact that the diameter of the cap barely exceeds the height of the stem. In most cases the Gill fungi have a small depression in the gill edge just a short distance from where it joins the stem. The stem goes right into the cap and is not easily removed, unlike the stem of the Parasol. Cut full-grown specimens—particularly Gill fungi—through the centre and see how the gills are placed in relation to the stem or cap; they may be disconnected from the stem, running along the stem, or else attached to it in a "winding" way. There is no vestige of a ring around the genus *Tricholoma*. The flesh of the Blewit is firm. Several kinds formerly included in this genus have been subdivided and included in a new genus. The gills (lamellae) often differ in colour, although the spores are white and/or rosy; they may range from a beautiful light yellow to ochre. Further examples are the Yellow Knight Fungus (*Tricholoma flavovirens*) and the Narcissus Blewit (*T. sulphureum*). A variation in smell is moreover noticeable in this genus. It can be best appreciated by sniffing at the gills of fresh specimens. The odour of the Narcissus Blewit has been compared with that of coal gas, as well as narcissus bulbs. The writer finds that coal gas or sulphur dioxide is nearer the mark. But it is idle to digress over differences in smell or taste. The Soap Blewit (*T. saponaceum*) definitely smells of soap. Other Blewits smell of flour or cucumber. Their taste may be mild or sharp. All these characteristics make it interesting for the beginner to start with the classification of the Blewit family. And the knowledge gathered here will be useful when studying other toadstools. It is also worth noticing the beautiful colour of cap and stem of the Blewits (Plate 3a).

19a. PINK NAIL. *Gomphi'dius rose'us* (Fr.) Karst.

Besides the olive-black to black spores, the genus *Gomphidius* is marked by its slimy cap and the thick, widely spaced gills running partially down the stem. The gills of full-grown specimens are seemingly covered with black dust owing to the dark spores. The young fungus has a membrane between the edge of the cap and the stalk, which remains like a ring around the stem when full grown.

The genus derives its name from the shape of the fungus, resembling an old-fashioned forged nail (*gomphos*).

The species pictured is one of the smallest—1¼ to 2 inches—of this genus; the cap is pink, the stalk whitish with a yellow foot. A remarkable fact is that the Pink Nail usually grows in close proximity to the Cow Boletus (*Su'illus bo'vinus* [L. ex Fr.] O.K., syn. *Ixo'comus bo'vinus* [L. ex Fr.] Quel., *Bole'tus bo'vinus* L. ex Fr.) (see right-hand side of picture). The Cow Boletus has a cap of 2 to 4 inches, well fleshed, yellowish brown to light auburn; it is sticky in humid weather and smooth and shiny when dry; it is, furthermore, flexible. The yellowish pores are angular and divided into smaller fractions by sunken partitions. The stalk is rather short and slender and has about the same colour as the cap.

The Cow Boletus can be found in pinewoods as well as on heaths near conifers.

19b. DOUGHNUT FUNGUS. *Rhizi'na undula'ta* Fr. ex. Fr., syn. *Rhizi'na infla'ta* (Schaeff.) P. Karst.

This species has proved to be a conifer parasite and is not common, though it may be found in pinewoods when there has been a fire in the wood. From these charred spots this Pocket fungus attacks the surrounding healthy conifers. The frail and waxy Cup fungus, semi-spherical when young, is irregularly bumpy and vaulted; the upperside is auburn to dark brown with a white margin which disappears when the fungus ages.

The hollow underside is yellowish white and has rootlike appendages attaching the fungus to the soil. This species may be 4¾ inches in diameter and 1¾ inches tall.

This fungus cannot be confused with other genera. It grows in pinewoods, not always in places where there has been a wood fire, and can be found between June and October.

19c. STICKY CORAL FUNGUS. *Calo'cera visco'sa* (Pers. ex Fr.) Fr.

This prettily coloured little wood fungus is common and grows at the base of coniferous stumps from summer until late autumn. The orange to golden colour is set off to advantage against the dark background.

The fruit-body—2 to 3¼ inches high—is tough and flexible, with antler-like to coral-shaped branchings, especially at the top. This species is very sticky in a moist atmosphere. The outer appearance may cause *Calocera viscosa* to be mistaken for a member of the Coral fungi.

The fruit-body is too cartilaginous and gelatinous for a Coral fungus. The *Calocera* genus actually belongs to the lignicolous Quivering fungi—Tremellaceae. The difference is also marked by its stickiness and its preference for conifers.

Confusion may be possible with the Little Yellow Horn (*Calocera cornea* [Batsch. ex Fr.] Loudon), which, however, is smaller—about ½ inch—has no branchings, and is yellower. This species usually grows on the decayed wood of broad-leaved trees.

The next genus, the Funnel fungi (*Clitocybe*), is not outstanding for spectacular shapes or colour; it is notable rather for the way in which the gills run along the stem, giving the impression that the stem merges into the cap. The funnel shape, not always noticeable, generally occurs when the specimen is fully grown. In the early stages the edge of the cap is mostly rolled inwards, and frequently the cap is more bowl-shaped than funnel-shaped. Here again its characteristics are most easily learnt by cutting one in half. The finest shapes are those of the Slender Funnel Fungus (*Clitocybe infundibuliformis*) and the Red-brown Funnel (*C. inversa*). One of the best known of the larger variety is the Mist Fungus (*C. nebularis*), which nearly always grows in clumps, sometimes within fairy rings.

Most of the genera so far mentioned (Milk fungi, *Amanita*, *Russula*, Parasol, Blewit, and Funnel fungi) grow on the ground; the next genus, *Collybia*, has a wide choice of substrata and in some cases even grows on other kinds of rotting toadstools.

According to new discoveries, many fungi formerly incorporated in *Collybia* have now been extended to other families. A useful characteristic to remember in field work is that the stem is tough, pipe-like, and flattened at the top. Of the variety which grows on other fungi, the Ochre Tuber (*Collybia cirrhata*) is a tiny white growth, only a few centimetres wide. A larger species, up to 4 inches, is the Spool Foot (*C. fusipes*), characterised by white lamellae set wide apart, pale pink to brown in colour and with a spool-like stem. The stem, thicker in the centre, becomes smaller below and ends in a striped, rather upturned end that is brown. This toadstool is mostly to be found at the foot of beeches.

Another genus, *Marasmius*, is notable and easily remembered for one characteristic. The stem is tough and like cartilage and can be bent without snapping. This variety can easily be dried and when damped comes to life again, resuming much of its former shape. Marasmia are mostly small toadstools, growing generally on wood, fallen branches, and pine needles. One of the best-known kinds is the Fairy-ring Champignon (*Marasmius oreades*), which can be found in meadows, grassy spots, or borders. Its colour varies from red-brown to leather yellow, according to the degree of dryness; with a diameter of up to 2 inches, it has widely spaced cream gills, with the stem the same colour as the cap. Its flesh and gills smell of bitter almonds. Its name indicates the fact that it usually grows in rings. While *Marasmius* is not particularly notable either for colour or shape, attention must be drawn to the Garlic Horn-stemmed toadstool (*M. scorodonius*). This small and undistinguished fungus smells and tastes of garlic when a piece is broken off. It grows mostly on fir needles, is red-brown to flesh-coloured, with creamy, widely spaced gills, and its stem is some 2 inches high. In countries where few mushrooms are cultivated for food, the Garlic toadstool is much esteemed as a flavouring. Owing to their toughness, these fungi can easily be dried and preserved.

20. FLY AGARIC. *Amani'ta musca'ria* (L. ex Fr.) Pers. ex S. F. Gray.

Most people recognise the Fly Agaric; it stands out almost defiantly in the forest with its red cap and white spots. We may take it as the prototype of *Amanita* in general. If we know the characteristic features of this genus, to which the most poisonous species belong, then we should avoid the mistake of confusing the deadly poisonous species with species belonging to other genera. Briefly, then, these features are: cap usually spotted, white gills, stalk with a ring or sleeve around it, and a swelling or bag on the lower part of the stalk.

To find the Fly Agaric, you must look under birches, for which it seems to have a special liking, or in pine forests. In America the Fly Agaric occurs under aspen, conifers, or in brushy places, including bramble patches. The cap, at first spherical, later spreading out, is between 6 and 8 inches in diameter, scarlet or pale to deep orange. The upper surface of the cap has white flakes which usually disappear when it rains. The yellowish flesh below the outer skin of the cap can be clearly seen in one of the illustrations. The gills are set close together and are white to yellowish, according to age. The stalk is solid at first, becoming hollow. Around the stalk, about two-thirds of the way up, is a broad white, drooping cuff. The lower part of the stalk is swollen and surrounded by warty wrinkles. This toadstool, though it certainly has poisonous properties, is not deadly poisonous. But it is not edible.

86

There are of course many other genera belonging to the Gill fungi, but it is not the intention of this book to mention them all. The bell-like caps of *Mycena* are attractive; so are those of *Panaeolus*, though these two are not the only campanulate genera. The spores may be white, black, pink, or brown.

Further groups or kinds are the Wax-gills (*Hygrocybe* or *Hygrophorus*) with their waxy gills and many-coloured caps: white, yellow, orange, and red. The Wax-gills inhabit almost exclusively grassy spots. The genus *Pleurotus* is characterised by the fact that the stem is at the side of the cap or is sometimes even nonexistent. Consequently the gills do not meet in the middle but at some point at the side of the cap. A well-known example is the Oyster Cap (*P. ostreatus*). Although the stem is off-centre, its function is the same. It ensures that when the spores fall from the fruit-body they can be distributed unhindered over a wide area.

The many genera producing brown spores may be passed over without comment, as they would need specialised study. To these belong the veiled fungi, already mentioned. The Ink fungi may be seen in Plate 27 a, b.

Having dealt shortly with some of the genera of the Gill fungi, let us turn to the other groups; they are particularly interesting since they deviate from the usual cap and stem forms.

The Pore fungi are fungi with fine holes or pores (the mouths of small tubes) on the underside of the cap. The hymenium which covers the gills in the Gill fungi is spread on the inner side of the tubes. Originally all the fungi with such pores—the *Boletus* and *Polyporus* species—were grouped together. It now appears that *Boletus*, although provided with pores, has greater affinity with the Gill fungi. On the border line between Gill fungi and boletes are the Curled-edge or *Paxillus* species, which, while possessing gills, have some typical bolete characteristics (Plate 16c).

To facilitate the distinction between these two groups, here is a short description of boletes. These are ground fungi, growing in woods, with a fleshy stem centrally placed and the hymenial tubes separating easily from the cap. When cut through, hymenium and cap are soon identified. With the possible exception of the Parasitic Boletus (*Xerocomus* [*Boletus*] *parasiticus*), they are not parasites (Plate 22a), although experts are divided in their opinions. Many edible toadstools belong to the bolete family, of which the Cep or Squirrel's Bread (*Boletus edulis*) immediately comes to mind. One particular characteristic in many of the species—noticeable in greater or lesser degree—is that broken off or damaged flesh turns blue when exposed to the air. This blue, notably in the Cep, may vary from light blue to indigo. Contrary to former belief, this colouring cannot determine whether or not the specimen is poisonous. When the pores of the Chestnut Boletus (*Xerocomus* [*Boletus*] *badius*) are pressed, they change from a greenish to a blue-green colour. Such ready means of identification are useful in field work.

The taste of a toadstool also helps to identify the species. The Pepper Boletus (*Suillus* [*Boletus*]

21a. YELLOW SMOOTH-EDGED RUSSULA. *Rus'sula ochroleu'ca* (Pers. ex Secr.) Fr.

This species is the most common among the various species of yellow-capped Russulas. The cap, 1½ to 4 inches in diameter, is convex at first, later becoming depressed in the centre, with a palish yellow to ochreous colour and a more or less smooth edge. The regularly growing gills are cream-coloured, with a somewhat darker reflection where the light falls on them obliquely. To observe this, it may be necessary to move the fungus slightly. The stem is uniformly thick, white to palish ochre, later slightly fading to grey. The flesh tastes a little acrid and sometimes may be almost tasteless. This Russula is common in pine-woods and deciduous forests in summer and autumn.

Other Russulas with a yellow surface on the cap and whitish gills which may be confused with the above-mentioned species are the Yellow Striped-edge Russula (*Rus'sula fel'lea* [Fr.] Fr.), the Yellow Birch Russula (*R. clarofla'va* Grove), and the Yellow Beech Russula (*R. sola'ris* Ferd. and Winge).

The cap of the Yellow Striped-edge Russula is pale ochre and clearly striated, often furrowed; gills, stem, and flesh are often ochre. The taste is very acrid. This species is common in deciduous forests, especially under beeches and oaks.

The Yellow Birch Russula, with its chrome yellow cap, can be found under birches and alders. The stem is whitish with a yellow base. The flesh has a mild taste and turns grey when exposed to the air. The Yellow Beech Russula is much smaller—1¾ to 2½ inches—and dark chromate-yellow, especially in the centre, with a lighter and striated edge. It tastes acrid. This species is found under beeches but is not common.

21b. THE SICKENER. *Rus'sula emet'ica* (Schaeff. ex Fr.) S. F. Gray.

The *Russula* genus has many brightly coloured species: reds of various shades, yellow, green, or variegated. According to mycologists, the Russulas are known to be difficult for easy identification so far as the species are concerned. The colours often fade greatly, especially the red ones. Species may often be correctly identified only by applying chemical reagents.

The specimen illustrated, however, has some distinctive features. The cap, sticky when damp, is bright red, usually fading to become almost colourless. The greater part of the cuticle is easily torn off from the flesh. The edge of the cap is at first smooth, later becoming striated. The diameter of the cap may reach 2¼ inches, though it is usually less. The gills are white and attached to the stem—a distinctive feature of the genus *Russula*. The white stem is rather short. The flesh has an acrid taste. This species is quite common to all kinds of woods, growing particularly between moss from summer until well into autumn. The Sickener is said to be poisonous, but no thorough research has been carried out. It is not advisable to test this species for edibility.

Among the many red Russulas, the Brittle Russula (*Rus'sula fra'gilis* [Pers. ex Fr.] Fr.) greatly resembles the species described above, though usually somewhat smaller and a less vivid red. The white gills are toothed (magnifying glass). The whole fungus is brittle, as the name indicates. The flesh also has an acrid taste. Naphthol changes the colour of the exterior of the stem to blue.

21c. SLENDER FUNNEL FUNGUS. *Clitocy'be infundibulifor'mis* (Schaeff. ex Weinm.) Quel.

This species justifies its name: it is slender and funnel-shaped. The funnel shape is associated with strongly decurrent gills and the fact that the stem gradually broadens out to the cap (see section). The cap is tan to ochreous, ochre-brown, and sometimes even red-ochreous. The thin-fleshed, silky, and felty Funnel Fungus, with a cap from 1½ to 2¾ inches, is spherical with an inrolled edge at first, later funnel-shaped with usually a central boss. The closely set gills are white to yellowish. The elastic stem has a lighter colour than the cap; the bottom of the stem is attached to leaves or needles by white down.

This fungus can be found in summer and autumn, usually in groups or in fairy rings. The smell of the flesh vaguely resembles that of bitter almonds. This species may be confused with the Red-brown Funnel Fungus (*Clitocy'be flac'cida* [Sow. ex Fr.] Kummer, syn. *Clitocy'be inver'sa* [Scop. ex Fr.] Quel., *Lepis'ta inver'sa* [Scop. ex Fr.] Pat.), which also grows in deciduous and coniferous woods. The cap is usually a pretty red-brown, whereas the stem and gills are darker than those of the Slender Funnel Fungus.

piperatus) tastes of pepper, the Bitter Boletus (*Tylopilus* [*Boletus*] *felleus*) is bitter, and the Cep or Squirrel's Bread has a nutty flavour. The pores, too, can be of differing kinds: small, large, or angular; white, pale yellow, rose, grey, orange to red.

The other porous group belongs to the Polyporaceae. In these the pores cannot be separated from the cap, although they may easily be distinguished in cross section. They grow mostly on trees or wood, usually without stems or with only short eccentrically placed ones. The stems are tough, gristly, or woody. The Giant Fungus (*Polyporus giganteus*), for instance, certainly lives up to its name. It really consists of broad overlapping "caps" placed one on top of the other. The fruit-body may reach a width of over a yard and weigh more than 100 pounds. These giants are found mostly at the feet of beech trees. The caps are banded, and the light-coloured pores when pressed turn dark brown. Of the fungi feared by foresters, the deadly Fir Murderer (*Fomes annosus*) eats away at the roots and feet of trees, especially firs. An extremely well-known species is the Elves' Seat (*Coriolus* [*Polyporus*] *versicolor*); it flourishes on all kinds of branches and stumps and is easily recognised by its crescent shape, absence of stem, its somewhat velvety cap—up to 3 inches in diameter—and by the coloured bands (yellow, blue-brown to black) with which it is adorned. The Topfungus (*Polystictus* [*Polyporus*] *perennis*), which grows on the ground and has a centrally placed cap, proves an exception to the rule that Polyporaceae are tree fungi. At first sight this type would not seem to be a Pore fungus, but a glance at the underside of the cap removes all doubt. The cap, thin-edged and up to 4 inches in diameter, is a leathery brown and often has light and darker bands. The stem is short and light-coloured and has a velvety texture. Several specimens may sometimes be found growing together.

Certain genera belonging to this group have no round or angular tubes, but the pores have the appearance of a maze. The best-known example is the Maze Fungus (*Daedalea quercina*), found on hardwood, chiefly oak, as well as on worked oak in houses. An examination of this bracket-shaped, cork-like fungus will reveal how apt is its name.

Closely related to the Maze Fungus is the Red-pored Wood Fungus (*D. confragosa*) shown in Plate 7c. These are but a few varieties of this large and multi-form group.

The life of a fungus fruit-body is generally short, although there are some that have a relatively long life span. In such cases, a new tube layer grows beneath the cap every year, covering that of the previous year. A good example is the False Tinderfungus (*Fomes igniarius*), in the beginning spherical or cushion-shaped, later taking the form of a console or horse's hoof; grey-brown above; very fine pores. The flesh, built up from old layers, is as hard as stone. The writer has a specimen which has been sawn through to enable him to count the layers, as is done with the yearly rings of trees. This particular fungus must have been at least twenty-two years old. The type is to be found mostly on poplars and willows. Very similar to this is the True Tinderfungus

22a. PARASITIC BOLETUS. *Xeroco'mus parasit'icus* (Bull. ex Fr.) Quel., syn. *Bole'tus parasit'icus* Bull. ex Fr.

This species is parasitic on another fungus, the Earthball (see below). The cap of the parasite is velvety in texture and dirty yellow to brownish. In the fully grown specimen the yellowish pores are wide and angular and run part of the way down the stalk. The stem, by which it is attached to its host, is yellow. Sometimes as many as ten specimens can be found on the one host. They are numerous every year. How the parasitism occurs is not yet known.

22b. EARTHBALL. *Scleroder'ma auran'tium* L. ex Pers., syn. *Scleroder'ma vulga're* Fr.

This fungus usually appears from June to November, especially in sandy forests, fields, and roadsides. Generally several are to be found together. It is not a Puffball in the mycological sense. Puffballs and Earthballs belong to the Gasteromycetes, as do Earthstars. In this order of fungi the spores are formed inside the plant and can escape only by an opening in the top of the fruit-body.

The Earthball is stalkless and irregularly spherical, up to 4 inches in breadth and somewhat less in height. The colour is pale to brownish yellow. In older specimens the outer skin breaks into small fragments which remain on the surface as rough scales. In the young plant the inside is filled with a white mass. As it ages and the spores ripen, this spore-forming tissue turns dark violet to blue-black. The smell of this dark mass is unpleasant.

This species can be confused with the Rooting Earthball (*Scleroder'ma verruco'sum* Pers.), the distinguishing features of which are its thinner skin, darker colour, and purplish-brown spore-bearing tissue. Furthermore, it has a somewhat wrinkled stem with numerous white mycelium strings. In spite of the Latin specific name, *verrucosum* (warty), its skin is less warty than that of *S. auran'tium*.

For the description of a species of *Boletus* parasitising the Earthballs, see the previous caption.

22c CHANTERELLE. *Cantharel'lus ciba'rius* Fr.

This is an easily recognised species. The whole plant is egg-yellow in colour with darker and lighter shades. The cap—3¼ inches in diameter—is at first spherical with its edges rolled under, and later funnel-shaped with a wavy or lobed margin. The underside does not have real gills, but folds which are rather widely spaced. The folds are thick, branched, and in places united. They continue for some distance down the stem, which is as though stuffed but thins towards its base. The inside flesh is yellow-white and has a faint smell of apricots or peaches. The plant tastes mild when young, later rather peppery. The Chanterelle appears between June and November in pine and deciduous forests. Formerly this species and the False Chanterelle (see below) were included in the same genus: *Cantharellus*. It was then found that these two species could not be of the same genus, since the folds of *C. cibarius* are not real gills in the mycological sense of the term, like those of the False Chanterelle. They both belong to the stalked fungi but are placed in quite different genera.

The False Chanterelle, formerly called *Cantharel'lus auranti'acus* Fr., or *Clitocy'be auranti'aca* (Fr. ex Wulf.) Studer, now bears the name *Hygrophorop'sis auranti'aca* (Wulf. ex Fr.) R. Maire. The cap is thinly fleshed, resembles chamois leather, and is orange-red with a down-rolled margin. The gills, a brighter orange-red, are closer together than the folds of the true Chanterelle, and the taste is not peppery. The false one occurs more often in pine forests and appears rather later in the year. It used to be regarded as a poisonous twin of *C. cibarius*, but it is merely less tasty.

(*Ungulina* [*Fomes*] *fomentaria*), formerly—and occasionally still—used in tinder boxes. *Fomes igniarius* is unsuitable as tinder on account of its hardness.

The species of Polyporaceae are less "fleshy" and can therefore be easily dried, maintaining their colours and shapes even when dry. There are many extremely interesting species in this group. One such is the Lacquer Fungus (*Ganoderma lucidum*), which is notable for its reddish or chestnut cap with side stem, glistening as though it has been lacquered. It grows on old branches and hardwood stumps.

The next family to be examined is that of the Spine fungi or Hydnaceae; it is characterised by the fact that under the "cap"—often absent—there are no tubes or gills but only spines to be seen. The hymenium is spread out over these. It is worth discussing specific kinds, as they are to be found almost everywhere and are easy to identify.

First is the Scaled Prickle Fungus (*Hydnum imbricatum*), a robust specimen with a short thick stem and a brown cap covered with darker upstanding scales. It is found mostly on sandy soil under fir trees. The Yellow Spine Fungus (*H. repandum*) has a cream to ochre cap and a lighter-coloured and very brittle stem. It is an excellent edible toadstool, growing in both deciduous and fir woods. Most of the Spine fungi grow on the ground, though there are kinds to be found on wood or fir cones. The most common of these is the Earspoon Fungus (*H. auriscalpium*), which chooses pine cones as its hosts. It is a small species with a leathery kidney-shaped cap $\frac{1}{2}$ to 1 inch wide, brownish-black in colour, with grey to brown spines. The stem—2 inches long—is at the side and is hard and brown. It is therefore easily recognisable, especially because of its partiality for pine cones and the curiously placed stem. The Spine fungi may be dried and many of them have a pleasant smell.

The Coral or Club fungi (Clavariaceae) clearly owe their name to their shape. Many well-formed and coloured species belong to this group. They may or may not be branched in shape; the branched species have forked or comb-like tops. The hymenium in this group is found on the outside of the fruit-body. To this group belongs the Field or Moor Club Fungus (*Clavaria argillacea*) (Plate 30b).

In the Crust fungi (Corticiaceae), the hymenium is spread on a flat or wrinkled surface. These fungi are in no way related to the previous groups. Most of them are thin, crust-like fungi growing almost exclusively on wood. Examples easy to recognise are the Yellow Crust (*Stereum hirsutum*), which looks like a yellow crust growing on all sorts of hardwood and also on worked wood, and the Violet Crust (*S. purpureum*). This last may be considered identical with the Yellow Crust except for colour. Amongst the varieties of this *Stereum* genus, there are some which, if scratched with a fingernail, give out a reddish fluid. Because of this they are also known as the bleeding Sterea.

23a. SULPHUR TUFT. *Hypholo'ma fascicula're* (Huds. ex Fr.) Kummer, syn. *Naematolo'ma fascicula're* (Huds. ex Fr.) Karst.

This toadstool grows in clusters from early summer until well into autumn, usually on trunks and stumps of broad-leaved trees and on conifers or seemingly on the soil, but in reality on dead roots. The bare cap, convex at first, and 1¼ to 2 inches wide, is sulphur-yellow, turning red-brown in the centre and often with dark remains of the curtain at the edge (see illustration). The gills are yellowish at first, then greenish yellow, and finally become green-brown violet because of their spores. The slender and curved stem, 2 to 3¼ inches long, is yellowish and brownish at the base. The flesh tastes bitter.

Confusion may occur with the Red Sulphur Tuft (*Hypholo'ma sublateri'tium* [Fr.] Quel., syn. *Naematolo'ma sublateri'tium* [Fr.] Karst.), which is also very common. The cap of this latter species is bigger and fleshier, and the centre is brick to yellow-red with a yellowish margin. The remains of the curtain at the edge of the cap are white to yellowish. The gills are yellow-grey, turning to olive-grey. The stem is yellowish with a red-brown base. The Red Sulphur Tuft grows exclusively on broad-leaved trees. The flesh tastes less bitter than that of the Sulphur Tuft. Another species of this genus—which may also be confused with the ordinary Sulphur Tuft—is the Common Birch Sulphur Tuft (*Hypholo'ma capnoi'des* [Fr. ex Fr.] Kummer, syn. *Naematolo'ma capnoi'des* [Fr. ex Fr.] Karst.), which is less common. Its cap—up to 2¼ inches—is yellowish to ochre, darker in the centre. The gills are pale yellow to bluish-grey (not greenish), later turning brownish. The thin stem, usually curved, is yellow-white at the top and ruddy brown at the base. The flesh tastes mild and is never bitter. All three species mentioned grow in clusters and have dark purple spores.

23b. HONEY FUNGUS. *Armilla'ria mel'lea* (Vahl. ex Fr.) Kummer, syn. *Armilla'riella mel'lea* (Vahl. ex Fr.) Karst.

This fungus is a very common and dangerous tree parasite which is often confused with the Scaly Cluster Fungus, described on page 58. The Cluster Fungus has sharper scales than the Honey Fungus, on the cap as well as on the stem. The ring is not whitish and disappears more quickly; the spores are brown, whereas the Honey Fungus has white ones.

The cap of the Honey Fungus, 2 to 6 inches wide, is either honey-coloured, yellow-brown, or olive to auburn and is covered with perishable black-brown scales thickly set in the centre. The shape is at first spherical but later flattens out. The gills, white to yellowish, turn red to brownish-mottled and have a decurrent tooth. The stem is tenacious and more or less grooved. The colour is yellow to brownish and often olive-yellowish at the base; the length is 6 inches. A white to yellowish ring stands away from the upper part of the stem. This is the remains of the velum partiale, which can be seen between the edge of the cap and the stalk of the young Honey Fungus.

This tree parasite can be found in summer and autumn growing in clusters either on living or dead deciduous wood or conifers, sometimes apparently on the bare soil, but in this case it is parasitising roots or buried wood.

The young specimen of the Honey Fungus is sometimes used for human consumption, but it is advisable not to eat the tough stem.

Another interesting group is that of the Quivering fungi (Tremellales), characterised by a gelatinous, jelly-like fruit-body. The variety in this group is quite extraordinary. A good example is the Brown Quivering Fungus (*Tremella foliacea*) (Plate 7a).

The Spine Quivering Fungus (*Tremellodon gelatinosum*) might easily be mistaken for a Spine fungus owing to the spines on the underside. It is a semicircular fungus with a short stem fixed at the side, growing on needle-leaved trees, stumps, and branches; the upper part is grey-brown to bluish, with light to light blue spines on the underside, the spines being shorter nearer the edge. To this same group belong the *Calocera* species—yellow to orange in colour—which look like and can easily be mistaken for Coral fungi (Plate 19c).

Among the fungi with stipes are some in which the spores are formed within the fruit-body and not outside it. These are the Paunch fungi or Gasteromycetes. In these fungi the ripe spores can escape only when the fruit-body bursts open. As long as the spores remain unripened, the fruit-body is closed. The inside of the fruit-body is then just a white mass and is called the gleba, or sporing tissue. When ripe, the spores darken.

The whole of the fruit-body is not always subservient to producing spores; there is often a part—the lowest—which is sterile and, in certain genera, looks like a stem. The best way to see this is to cut through an advanced-stage Puffball; it will then be easy to see the difference between the spore-forming part and the other. The sterile part remains after the fertile part has burst open. A good example may be seen in Plate 28a.

To the Paunch fungi belong the Puffballs, the beautiful Earthstars and Nest fungi, the Earthball and False Truffles, the Stemmed Puffballs, and the Stinkhorns.

The False Truffles have much the same shape as the true Truffles, but nothing else in common, particularly from a gastronomic point of view. The true Truffles belong to quite a different class, the Sac fungi or Ascomycetes, while the False Truffles (such as *Rhizopogon*) belong to the Basidiomycetes. But both False and true Truffles grow more or less underground. The False Truffles are unsuitable for eating.

The bursting open of the fruit-body among the Paunch fungi is not uniform. In the Puffballs the rent in the fruit-body occurs in the upper part; in the case of the Earthball (*Scleroderma*), with its thick tough skin (Plate 22b), the rent is irregular, allowing the black spore mass to escape. The False Truffles shed their spores through the rotting of the encircling wall when the spores are fully grown. In the Bird's Nest fungi (Nidulariales), so called because of their shape, the spores occur within flat round discs, called peridioles, which lie in the cup-shaped fruit-body. The peridioles are flung out by raindrops, which also help to release the spores of Puffballs and the like. Every drop of rain falling on the papery wall of the fruit-body causes it to contract like a bellows and blow out a cloud of spores. In the Bird's Nest fungi, the funnel-like nest or perid-

24a. CEP. *Bole'tus ed'ulis* Bull. ex Fr.

But for the Chanterelle, the stout Cep is the toadstool best known for its edible qualities. This species can be found in all kinds of woods from early summer until autumn. The cap of this big and fleshy bolete may reach a width of 8 inches or more. The shape is semi-globular, and the colour may have all the shades ranging from fawn to dark brown. The narrow pores are white to begin with but later change to yellow to greenish yellow and do not change colour when pressure is applied.

The layer of tubes can be easily separated from the flesh of the cap, as is the case with all boletes. The massive stem, up to 4¾ inches long, is whitish to pale brown and generally clearly swollen at the bottom. The upper part has a network of whitish raised lines which fade away with age.

The flesh has a nutty flavour and is permanently white, though slightly pinkish under the cuticle, the latter not easily removed. A darker variety of this species (*Boletus pini'cola*), with an auburn cap, can be found in pinewoods.

Confusion may be possible with the Bitter Boletus (*Tylo'pilus fel'leus* [Bull. ex Fr.] Karst., syn. *Bole'tus fel'leus* Bull. ex Fr.), which grows in pinewoods. This species has a brownish network on a slim stem and whitish pores soon turning pink. The tubes remain free from the stem. The white flesh, discolouring to pink, tastes bitter, and this makes it unfit for human consumption.

Another fungus that may be confused with the Cep is the Chestnut Boletus (*Xero'comus badius* [Fr.] Gilbert, syn. *Bole'tus badius* Fr.), which is smaller. This latter species also has a dark brown cap, but the pale yellow to greenish pores become bluish green when pressure is applied; the fawn-coloured slim stem is cylindrical and possesses no network.

24b. VERDIGRIS AGARIC. *Stropha'ria aerugino'sa* (Curt. ex Fr.) Quel.

When this toadstool, with its dark spores, has its characteristic colour it is easy to identify; but with aged specimens, spoiled by rain, this is rather hard.

The cap, 1¼ to 3¼ inches wide, is at first bell-shaped and later expanded with a centre boss and covered with a thick, bluish-green slime, often with whitish scales.

The edge of the cap sometimes shows white remains of the partial veil (velum partiale). When the toadstool is aging, the slimy coating usually disappears, revealing the yellow background, with here and there some traces of green. The broad gills have at first a light colour but gradually turn purple-brown.

The stem is also blue-green and has a perishable ring below which the stem is provided with little white scales or flakes. The flesh tastes and smells faintly like radish.

This beautiful toadstool grows in all kinds of woods and in the grassy verge along paths from summer until well into autumn.

24c. VELVET BOLETUS. *Xeroco'mus subtomento'sus* (L. ex Fr.) Quel., syn. *Bole'tus subtomento'sus* L. ex. Fr.

The picture shows the undersurface of the cap of a young specimen (right) and an old one (left) of this species of *Boletus*. Note the differences in colour and shape; the right-hand one is lemon-yellow and roundish, and the left-hand one darker and more angular.

The cap of the Velvet Boletus is brown, olive-coloured, and velvety in texture, 2 to 4¾ inches wide; the stem is fairly slender and yellow-brown.

The closely related Redfoot Velvet Boletus (*Xero-co'mus chrysen'teron* [Bull. ex St. Amans] Quel., syn. *Bole'tus chrysen'teron* Bull. ex St. Amans) has a cap of about the same colour, but there are cracks on the surface with a yellow to reddish background. The stalk—the base in particular—has a reddish hue.

Both species grow in deciduous woods and pinewoods.

ium is at first covered by a thin membrane. When this membrane is removed, the funnel with its discs looks like a nest with eggs—hence the name. When the Earthstars are fully grown, a central structure can be very distinctly seen; this is the innermost peridium, or endoperidium, in which the spores lie with the outer peridium, or exoperidium, around them. The fleshy exoperidium surrounds the paper-like endoperidium when young, so that the Earthstar, as yet not fully grown, looks like a tulip or crocus bulb—according to its size. When fully developed, the outer peridium splits into many slits which bend outwards. At the top of the endoperidium is an opening—the peristome—through which the spores can escape. In one species there are a number of openings, so that the apt name of Pepperpot (*Myriostoma* [*Geastrum*] *coliforme*) has been given to it. Distinguishing the Earthstars are the shape of the peristome and whether or not the endoperidium has a stem. They are often to be found on sandy soil.

Although the Stinkhorns belong to the Gasteromycetes group, they differ considerably in shape from the other genera of this group (Plate 6a). The spores are enclosed in a peridium when formed, but in full-grown specimens can be seen at the top of the stem. The Stinkhorn is a true Gasteromycete only in its "egg" stage. After that the stalk grows upwards, bursting the peridium, and the spores are entirely uncovered. At first the cap is covered with a greenish slime containing the spores. Flies are attracted to and eat this green slime and so help to disperse the spores.

It is evident from the varied assortment of genera, chosen arbitrarily here, what variety exists among these chlorophyll-lacking representatives of the plant world.

The intention of this book is to awaken interest and evoke a desire to get to know these "visions of the wood," as they have poetically been described. Anyone wandering through the countryside can see for himself that fungi not only grow in woods but also in meadows and gardens; the expression "children of darkness" therefore no longer describes them. In the times when toadstools were linked with serpents, vipers, and the devil, such expressions were well founded. Each kind of fungus has its own preference, such as the dampness of the ground and the quality of the soil, be it chalky, lacking in chalk, sandy, or clay. Both the substratum on which they will grow and their liking for certain types of trees vary. Stinkhorns, for instance, prefer a soil rich in nitrates. Other types of fungi will choose only dung, but then only the dung of plant-eating animals. Burnt patches of ground sometimes provide interesting finds.

When collecting fungi it is a good idea to note by which tree and under what conditions the specimen has been found. Experience shows that certain sorts will grow only in pine forests, others in deciduous woods, and sometimes under only one particular kind of tree. Good examples are the Birch Boletus and the Larch Boletus. The collector's early enthusiasm may lead him to forget this detail and so be faced later with problems of classification.

25a. AMETHYST FUNGUS or RED CABBAGE FUNGUS. *Lacca'ria amethy'stina* (Bull. ex Merat) Murr., syn. *Lacca'ria laccata*, var. *amethy'stina* (Vaill.) B. & Br.

This little fungus used to be taken for a variety of the Hoax Fungus (*Lacca'ria lacca'ta* [Scop. ex Fr.] Cooke), which is very common, but nowadays is regarded as a separate species. This wholly violet fungus cannot be confused with any other species except, perhaps, the Fairy Screen (*Myce'na pu'ra* [Pers. ex Fr.] Kummer). The latter fungus does not possess widely spaced gills and is remarkable for its radish-like smell; its colour is not as intense a violet as that of the Amethyst.

The colour of the Amethyst Fungus varies from light to vivid violet, according to exposure and conditions: sunny, shaded, dry, or moist. As mentioned before, the cap—up to 2 inches in diameter—the thick, distant gills, and the fibrous, tough stalk—up to 2½ inches long—are violet.

The cap, usually depressed in the centre, has a more or less wavy edge. The gills of the full-grown specimen seem to be covered with white dust; this dust is the spores.

The Hoax Fungus has much the same shape as the Amethyst Fungus, but the cap, gills, and stalk are auburn to flesh-coloured.

25b. BIRD'S NEST FUNGUS. *Cruci'bulum lae've* Bull. ex DC., syn. *Cruci'bulum vulga're* Tul.

After a careful study of this picture, it will be easy to identify this interesting little fungus when it is encountered in the open fields. Moreover, the Bird's-nest Fungus can be found on rotting wood and very often on old sacks, wood chips, and thatched roofs.

An extensive description would be superfluous. The little cup-shaped Nest fungus is ½ inch high and wide. The outside is yellowish and downy in texture, internally whitish and smooth.

At the bottom of the cup, covered with a membrane when the fungus is young, are small discs—peridioles—containing the spores.

25c. WHITE CORAL FUNGUS. *Clavuli'na crista'ta* (Holmskj. ex Fr.) J. Schroet., syn. *Rama'ria crista'ta* (Holmskj. ex Fr.) Quel., *Clava'ria crista'ta* Holmskj. ex Fr.

The White Coral Fungus can be found in all kinds of woods, ditches, on humus, or in grass, and is fairly common. This pretty little Coral fungus—up to 2½ inches tall—grows in different shapes and colours.

A short tenacious stem forms the foot of many smooth branches, which are flattened at the end with sharply pointed and crested tips. As noted earlier, the colour is variable, usually white or cream-coloured, but also grey to ashy.

Because of the pointed tips it is easy to identify this Coral fungus among other whitish to greyish, branched species.

We greatly hope that this book will encourage many to make the effort to get to know these products of nature. The careful descriptions of the fungi illustrated in the book should make it possible for the reader to compare the fungi found with the illustrations, and so identify them. In this way details will become familiar and eventually a mental picture will form of a particular fungus "from youth to age." The reader will appreciate that in the descriptions given here, we have chosen the middle path, since small differences in colour, shape, or size will be encountered between growing specimens and the illustrations. One other observation regarding colour: depending on weather conditions, the development from youth to age often brings changes in colour shades with it; the disappearance of a slimy covering may also reveal another colour. A typical case is the Copper-green Fungus (*Stropharia aeruginosa*) where, after the disappearance of the blue-green slime (whether through rain or damp), the yellow undercoat is exposed.

The only way to observe such variations in colour is to collect several specimens in various stages of development and not to rely entirely on the descriptions given in books.

THE ENLARGEMENT OF THE SURFACE OF THE HYMENIUM

An examination of the surface of a Gill, Pore, or Spine fungus soon enables us to see that the surface is enlarged through lamellae, tubes, or spines. Were the underside of a mushroom smooth, its capacity for producing spores would be much reduced. This is true of many Crust fungi, as well as unbranched Club fungi. The Quivering fungi achieve a greater surface area by their crinkled structure, and the spines of the Spine fungi make it possible for more spores to be produced. With the Pore fungi, where the hymenium covers the inner side of the tubes, an increased surface is thereby gained which may multiply its spore-producing capacity by 40. The great variation occurs in the case of the Gill fungi, which can be best illustrated by comparing a Wax-gill with an Amanita. In the first, the gills are wide apart, in the Amanita close together. The increase of surface may thereby vary between 4 to 20 times. A closer examination of the position of the lamellae shows that, in addition to the gills which run from the edge of the cap to the stem, there are others which lie between the gills and do not reach the stem, or are placed forkwise.

26a & b. PARASOL MUSHROOM. *Macrolepio'ta pro'cera* (Scop. ex Fr.) Sing., syn. *Lepio'ta pro'-cera* (Scop. ex Fr.) S. F. Gray.

This spectacular and, above all, graceful fungus is striking not only because of its size but also because of its beautiful markings on cap and stem. The species is one of the biggest among the Gill fungi. The cap of a full-grown specimen is spread out like an umbrella and may reach a diameter of 12 inches—sometimes even 16 inches—though the average size is 8 inches.

The young mushroom resembles a fist-sized drumstick before it expands. At this stage the underside of the cap is covered with a membrane, the partial veil, which remains like a ring around the stem of the full-grown specimen.

The cap is covered with thick brown scales over the central prominence. These scales are the remains of the cuticle, which tears into fragments (scales) when the fungus grows longer. They are not easily removed, in contrast to the scales of the Amanitas. The soft white gills grow closely together and free from the stem. The stem is slender and hollow, bulbous at the base. It has a movable cuff and tiger-striped markings.

The Parasol Mushroom is rather common from summer until October and grows in clearings in woods, verges, pastures, and gardens. At the left-hand side of the illustration is a young specimen, and at the right-hand side a full-grown one.

Confusion may be possible with the Tuber Parasol Mushroom (*Macrolepio'ta rhaco'des* [Vitt.] Sing., syn. *Lepio'ta rhaco'des* [Vitt.] Quel.). This fungus is more stunted, has coarser scales on the cap and no markings on the stem. Besides the bulbous base of the stem, also distinctive is the flesh of every part of this mushroom, which, when damaged or bruised, turns reddish. The Tuber Parasol Mushroom is to be found in the same places as the Parasol and also in pinewoods. Both species make good eating when young, preferably without the stem.

26c. POINTED-SCALE PARASOL FUNGUS. *Lepio'ta acutesqua'mosa* (Weinin.) Gillet.

This Gill fungus, which has both a nasty taste and smell, can be found in parks, gardens, and all kinds of woods. The cap, conical to spherical at first, later becoming somewhat expanded, is between 2½ and 4¾ inches wide and rather lumpy in the middle. The light-coloured surface of the cap is covered with closely set scales which are dark brown, conical, sharp, and straight—more or less concentrically arranged.

The closely growing gills are at first white and later turn brownish.

The stem, up to 4 inches long, is bulbous at the base, palish, and covered with only a few scales; the colour above the drooping ring is whitish. This drooping cuff is the remains of the membrane stretching out from stem to edge in the young stage of the fungus.

The scales in the cap are not the remains of the complete veil (velum universale), as is the case with the Amanitas. This species is easily identified and can be found in the above-mentioned places from summer until autumn.

As this toadstool usually appears in groups, the process of development is easy to follow.

MYCORRHIZA

We have already mentioned earlier (page 5) that many toadstools prefer certain trees and can usually be found if their preferences are known. Today a better understanding of the reason for such preferences has been reached. As so often—with the discovery of penicillin, for example—this fact was accidentally discovered, although research was being specifically directed towards the connection between trees and certain fungi. The German botanist A. B. Frank discovered the connection by accident at the end of the last century. He had been requested by his government to study a possible method of stimulating the growth of truffles. His research proved that truffles were always to be found under beech or oak trees. He therefore concentrated on the roots of these trees, since truffles are underground fungi. He noticed that the young roots of the beech and oak were different in some aspects from other tree roots. Under the microscope they appeared to be thicker and pronged, as well as being wound about with threads of mould or mycelium. The name "mycorrhiza" is particularly apt, as it means "fungus root."

It is especially through the later work—mostly carried out in laboratories—of the Swedish Professor E. Melin and his colleagues that many kinds of fungi are now known whose mycelia form mycorrhiza with the roots of certain trees. This was confirmed by growing both spawn and the tree as sterile cultures, bringing the two together and then studying the result. One of the most common examples and one which can easily be confirmed in nature is the Birch Boletus, which can be found only under birch trees. The Larch Boletus has formed a relationship with the larch, and the Fly Agaric with birch and fir. Notes of this kind—so long as one knows the individual fungi—make collecting more interesting and give it depth. It is evident that the last word as to the method of mycorrhiza formation has not been pronounced and that many questions still require answers. Try the experiment of uncovering the young roots of a beech in the hope of being lucky enough to find a root enveloped in fungus threads.

THINGS WORTH KNOWING ABOUT FUNGI

Fungi spores are extremely small and their diameter is measured in thousandths of millimetres. A thousandth of a millimetre is called a micron and represented by μ. In scientific works on fungi, length and breadth of spores are given in microns, as observed under the microscope, and they vary between 3 and 30 microns. It is impossible to examine these spores with the naked eye

27a. SHAGGY INK-CAP. *Copri'nus coma'tus* (Müll. ex Fr.) S. F. Gray.

As the Shaggy Ink-cap nearly always grows in groups, the various stages between youth and deliquescing aged specimens are clearly perceptible. From its appearance above the soil to the remaining bare stem after the dissolving of the gills, usually only 24 hours elapse. The white cap of this species, which can be easily identified from the illustration, is round and oviform at first, then spreads out to a cone or bell shape with a somewhat outcurved edge.

When young the cap is silky and fibrillose in texture, later covered with white and brown scales, standing away and flat; the top of the cap usually has a bare, brown spot. The closely packed gills are white at the young stage, but soon turn pink from the edge inwards, purple-pink to brownish, and finally completely black; at this stage they liquefy to an inky substance. The cap may stand as high as 4 inches; the slender white and hollow stem, up to 8 inches, has a perishable ring.

The Shaggy Ink-cap is very common and grows in pastures and rich soil, dung-heaps, gardens and parks, fields, along paths, and (see illustration) even along grassy kerbstones. It is found from early summer until autumn. The species is edible when young.

27b. FURROWED INK-CAP. *Copri'nus plica'tilis* (Curt. ex Fr.) Fr.

This very fragile fungus is common and grows in pastures, along paths, and in gardens from early summer until autumn. The full-grown specimen shown in the picture has been photographed from above to show the furrowed cap clearly. The cap is fairly translucent, between ½ and ¾ inches in diameter, grey-blue and at a young stage, oval to bell-shaped. Later it flattens and splits; it has a little ochre boss in the centre of its cap.

The gills are fixed to a little disc at the stem, which is whitish. The stem is between 2½ and 4 inches long.

27c. FIELD MUSHROOM. *Agar'icus campes'tris* L. ex Fr., syn. *Psallio'ta campes'tris* (L. ex Fr.) Quel

The Field Mushroom and the Horse Mushroom are the fungi which are most gathered and appreciated for their eating qualities. Most cases of fungi poisoning occur because these species are confused with the deadly poisonous Death Cap, which often is light-coloured. It is advisable to bear well in mind all the qualities of these species and to examine them again after bringing any home. (Note again the description of the Death Cap on page 10.)

The very variable Field Mushroom has a white cap —sometimes yellowed and turning brown with age— which is smooth and silky but sometimes covered with closely packed little brownish scales (never *patches* on the cap). When young, the cap is semi-spherical, later becoming vaulted, up to 4¾ inches wide, and thickly fleshed. The gills, when very young covered by a velum partiale, are at first white, then turn pale pink to flesh-coloured, finally becoming a uniform chocolate brown to black. The smooth silky stem, up to 2¾ inches long, is whitish, though often a bit yellow at the base, and has a thin white cuff, usually turned in at the edge. The flesh is white but may turn slightly red when damaged; it has a pleasant taste as well as smell. The Field Mushroom can be found from June to October and grows in manured pastures (in particular where horses feed), fields, and gardens.

The Horse Mushroom (*Agar'icus arven'sis* Schaeff. ex Secr., syn. *Psallio'ta arven'sis* [Schaeff. ex Secr.] Kummer) is more or less oviform to semi-globular at a young stage, though later flattens out and is fleshy. The cap is white and as a rule covered with yellow stains; it discolours to yellow when pressure is applied and is smooth and silky-sheened. The closely set gills are at first grey-pink, then turning from brownish red to chocolate. The slender white stem—also turning yellow when pressure is applied—is somewhat bulbous at the base and has a drooping cuff consisting of two layers, of which the lower one is indented in a star-like fashion. The flesh tastes mild and rather nutty, remains white, and usually has an aniseed-like smell.

This species can be found on the outskirts of woods and in parks, as well as in the same places as the first mentioned species.

and, as mentioned earlier, they must be collected en masse to observe their colour. Only with the help of a microscope can their shape be studied and reproduced in drawings. The author has observed with a strong magnifying lens the black spores on the grey gills of the ordinary Stained Gill Fungus (*Panaeolus campanulatus*). It is a bell-like toadstool on a long hollow stem, ribbed above, and up to 6 inches high. The cap is greyish, grey-brown (up to 1½ inches wide), sometimes with a whitish, notched veil around the edge. This kind grows mostly on dung in meadows and similar places.

Without the use of expensive apparatus we can try an experiment in order to see spores.

It has already been mentioned that the spores of the Gill fungi and the Pore fungi are shot off the basidium. In the case of the Gill fungi, the spores fall down between the lamellae; in the Pore fungi they fall through the tubes. After leaving the sterigmata to which they were bound, they travel a short way horizontally, then fall straight down, owing to the pull of gravity. But the fall is slow. All that is needed for the experiment is a large fullgrown Gill fungus—a Fly Agaric will do—or a pored species such as the Saddle fungus; a glass jar or a tumbler—not too thick—and an electric torch. Place the full-grown (and so spore-producing) fungus over the opening of the glass jar, having first removed the stem. Make sure that the cap lies perfectly horizontal so that its natural position is approximated. After leaving the fungus a short while in complete darkness, direct the light onto the jar or glass, and you will see the spores slowly falling; these minute structures can be seen with the naked eye by the light which they reflect. In the absence of a glass jar or tumbler, the cap may rest on two supports, but the disadvantage here is that the slightest draught will blow them away. When this experiment has been carried out, it will not be surprising to learn that a large mushroom sheds about 10,000 spores per second and that this rain of spores may last several days. It is understandable that millions of spores are produced and also that not all of them find a suitable place in which to germinate. The rate of descent is from 0.3 to 0.6 millimetres per second, according to the size of the spores. The number of spores released has been calculated by A. H. R. Buller; after experimenting he found that the Dryad's Saddle (*Polyporus squamosus*) produced 11,000,000,000 spores in 13 days (Plate 2a), and the Giant Puffball (*Calvatia maxima*, syn. *Bovista gigantea*) produced 2,000,000,000,000, a number which might be higher according to the size of the fruit-body. Fantastic though these figures are, millions of spores are lost before a single one finds a suitable spot on which to develop into a mycelium.

These experiments may be carried out with Stipe fungi, and similarly with the Sac fungi. We have already mentioned that in the larger kind, ripe ascopores are shot out like a cloud and that the bursting of the asci sounds like a soft rustle. A further experiment—effective even with the smaller Cup fungi— is the following: Enclose the fungi in a tin with damp paper; on the following day the lid should be removed. A small sharp tap against the side of the tin will result in the

28a. MOSAIC PUFFBALL. *Calva'tia uteri'formis* (Bull. ex Pers.) M. Moser, syn. *Calva'tia Bovi'sta* Pers., *Lycop'erdon caela'tum* Bull.

The name Mosaic Puffball is explained by the photograph, in which the division of the surface into small angular areas is clearly seen. The brown specimen is an old fungus from the previous year. It is remarkable to find an old and new specimen growing side by side; they are probably from the same mycelium.

In this group of fungi—the Puffballs or Gasteromycetes—the spores are formed inside the fruit-body. The Mosaic Puffball is one of the biggest species of this group, only the Giant Puffball (*Calva'tia gigan'tea* Pers.) being bigger, with a diameter of up to 20 inches. In the Mosaic Puffball the height and breadth are almost equal: about 6 inches. At first white in colour, it later turns ochre and finally brown. In the young plant the polygonal divisions are not at first visible; as it grows older, however, the outer coat of the upper part divides into little lozenges or rhomboids. The upper part, in which the spores are formed, is clearly differentiated from the lower. The latter is really the stalk and usually remains as a brown bowl for the rest of the year. The inside of the upper part is at first white, but with the ripening of the spores becomes an olive-brown mass. The spore-containing upper part tears away irregularly from above, thus allowing the spores to scatter. The upper part finally disappears.

This species is to be found in summer and autumn, mainly in grassy places among the dunes, on fields, or on the edges of forests.

28b. EARTH TONGUE. *Geoglos'sum cookeia'num* Nann.

To find Earth Tongues, you must look in grassy areas for black club-shaped or spindle-shaped fungi. They grow about 2 inches high. There are several species, all very similar, for they all have more or less the same form and colour: club-shaped, somewhat flattened, and black. Beginners find it difficult to distinguish the different species, and to identify a species with any accuracy a microscope may be required. The paraphyses of these fungi are then seen to differ considerably from one another. One species, however, can be identified with the naked eye: the Shaggy Earth Tongue (*Geoglos'sum hirsu'tum* Pers. ex Boudier), which is covered with small black hairs.

In view of the difficulties of identification, detailed descriptions of the various species are hardly worthwhile. The general term Earth Tongue should be satisfactory. Confusion with very similar fungi and especially with the Truffle Club Fungus (*Cor'dyceps ophioglossoi'des*) is certainly possible. In this species the transition from the spore-bearing part to the stem is more distinct than in the Earth Tongues. The colour is at first greenish-yellow, changing later to black. A further characteristic is the texture of the upper part, which is coarse and granular. A very important distinguishing feature is that the Truffle Club Fungus is parasitic on Stag Truffles (Elaphomyces), which, like all Truffles, are below ground. When you find the Truffle Club Fungus, you must dig really deep before you come to the Stag Truffle.

28c. SCARLET WAX-GILL. *Hygroph'orus puni'ceus* (Fr.) Fr.

The shiny, slippery cap is 2 to 4 inches in diameter and conical in shape. As it grows older, the cap widens out and the upper surface becomes discoloured. At first scarlet to blood-red, it fades through orange to yellow. The fairly stout stalk, up to 3¼ inches long, soon becomes hollow and striated; it is yellow to orange, growing toward the base. This species appears between late summer and late autumn in grassy areas, parks, forest clearings, and on damp fields. The scarlet *Hygroph'orus* is one of the largest of the species.

Do not confuse this toadstool with the Carmine Wax-gill (*H. coccin'eus* Fr.), which is smaller, with a redder stalk that is not streaked, or with the Vermilion Wax-gill (*H. minia'tus* [Fr.] Fr.), whose cap is not more than 1¼ inches in diameter, spherical, and vermilion in colour with fine scales; the stalk is thin and orange-red.

discharge, and the cloud of spores will thus be seen—better than under any other circumstances. In some cases, warmth may produce the same results, and also the introduction of drier air into the tin. In other cases, the asci may have already shot off their spores, which will then have adhered to the lid of the tin, especially if this is smeared with glycerine or vaseline beforehand. A strong beam of light will accelerate the movement.

In Gill fungi it is clear that a critical minimum distance between lamellae is necessary to give the spores the opportunity to fall; these gills also must be vertical. The drawings reproduced here from Buller's *Researches on Fungi* makes it clear why we insisted earlier that the toadstool must rest in its natural position. If this does not happen, the spores—after travelling a very short way horizontally—fall on the opposite or on the same gills (according to the direction of the tilt). This diagram makes it obvious that in the case of a 30° tilt the chances are that one fifth of the spores do not land in the open space intended. In any experiments along these lines, it is easy to discover what degree of tilt will prevent any spores from falling.

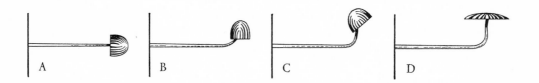

There is no problem about fungi with stems, for the stem regulates the position of the gills in relation to the ground. For fungi growing out of a hole in a tree, the stem bends itself in such a way that the position of the cap ensures that the lamellae are vertical. In this connection, attention is again drawn to the lateral stems of many fungi growing on wood, such as the Dryad's Saddle and Oyster Cap (*Pleurotus ostreatus*). The stem has an important part to play in the dispersal of spores; in addition, the length of the stem allows air currents to act upon the falling spores.

Whenever a vertically growing stem is placed in a horizontal position it will, by a growth curvature, tend to revert to the vertical. Buller has made many experiments along these lines.

Buller used a small variety of Ink-cap (*Coprinus plicatilis*). This elegant and delicate fungus may be described as follows: cap up to 1¾ inches, grey in colour but yellowish to ochre in the centre, deeply furrowed, transparent; the stem is about 4 inches long and structurally delicate; it grows on grassy spots.

The process of the spreading out of the cap lasted 9½ hours. In another experiment, also with a small Ink fungus, the cap reverted to a horizontal position after 17½ minutes. Should the reader wish to carry out a similar experiment, he should not choose too old a specimen; the best results

29a. PEPPERPOT. *Myrio'stoma colifo'rme* (Dicks. ex Pers.) Corda.

This toadstool belongs to the Puffballs (Gasteromycetes) and grows sparsely on dunes; up to the present this is the only place where it has been found (autumn). It bears a clear relationship to the Earthstar (*Gea'strum trip'lex*), described and shown on page 126.

The genus *Geastrum*, however, has only one opening in the endoperidium, whereas the genus *Myriostoma* has several. The full-grown Pepperpot—not a bad name—may be up to 6 inches in diameter. The exoperidium is about halfway divided into 6 to 10 lappets.

The papery endoperidium, up to 1¼ inches wide, contains the spores. It has many little holes on top and rests on numerous irregular little stalks.

29b. COMMON PUFFBALL. *Lycop'erdon perla'tum* Pers., syn. *Lycop'erdon gemma'tum* Fr.

This Puffball, which is very common—2½ to 4 inches tall and 2 inches wide—belongs to the family of the Lycoperdaceae and can be found in woods, on heaths, and in pastures, generally growing in groups. The whole toadstool, covered with little white prickles or warts, is at first white but changes to yellow or brown later. The shape is that of a reversed bottle or vase. The upper part is more or less spherical and is set more thickly with pointed prickles than the stem. They are easy to remove (a distinctive mark) and soon wash away when it is raining. The stem is cylindrical, more porous and tougher than the spore-forming upper part.

The spherical part opens at maturity. The spores of such a ripe specimen are easy to perceive by tapping this spore-forming part.

The stalk is sterile.

The fertile and the sterile part can be clearly distinguished when a mature or almost mature specimen is cut open.

29c. LANTERN FUNNEL-FUNGUS. *Omphalo'tus olea'rius* (DC. ex Fr.) Sing., syn. *Clitocy'be olea'ria* (DC. ex Fr.) R. Maire, *Clitocy'be illu'dens* (Schw.) Sacc.

The Lantern Funnel-fungus is a South European species and grows at the feet of or on the roots of olive, chestnut, and oak trees. The whole fungus is orange to brown-red-orange. The cap, up to 4¾ inches wide, is spherical at first, funnel-shaped with a central boss later on, and has a curved-back edge. The closely set gills are somewhat lighter and run down the stem, which tapers down to a pointed base. The gills of not too aged specimens phosphoresce in the dark (a greyish-green glimmer). This is why it is called Jack o'Lantern in the United States and Canada.

The Lantern Funnel-fungus is poisonous, and small specimens may be confused with the False Chanterelle (*Hygrophorop'sis auranti'aca* [Wulf. ex Fr.] Maire apud Martin-Sans, syn. *Clitocy'be auranti'aca* [Wulf. ex Fr.] Studer). The former species, however, grows in clusters.

are obtained from a small specimen with a thin, long stem. These can be found anywhere, and there is no need to search the woods for them. With no definite purpose in mind, we allowed toadstools to lie overnight and noticed in the morning that the stems had become crooked. This demonstrates how great is the tendency of the stem to bring the cap back to a normal position.

In many ways the manner of liberation of the spores of the Ink-caps is different from that of other Gill fungi. We noticed that after a day or two little of the original beauty of the Ink-cap is left. The white gills—also most of the cap—disappear, and what remains is a wet, dripping mess. What has happened?

Many kinds of Ink-caps are to be found in gardens, along roads, on dung-heaps and other spots rich in nitrogen. As an example, let us take the Shaggy Ink-cap (*C. comatus*). In its young stage it has the following characteristics: cap up to 6 inches, cylindrical or egg-shaped, colour white with darker upstanding scales, and often a bare yellow-brown spot on the top. The stem, which may be 8 inches high, is hollow, slender, and surrounded by a ring. At this stage the lamellae are still white, but later they turn rosy, becoming black and finally deliquescing.

While the gills are changing colour, something unusual is happening. The edge of the cap begins to curl upwards; this allows the spores at that spot to fall out. That part of the lamellae bereft of spores—and thus now superfluous—begins to deliquesce into a black mass, thus enabling another section of spores to fall out until most of the cap has disappeared. The spores fall just as in other Gill fungi and are not swallowed up in the watery mess. An experiment with a strong beam of light as previously outlined will show the falling of the spores. The black mass, when seen under a microscope, shows only a very few spores which in some way have still adhered.

HINTS FOR THE COLLECTION

A few hints may be useful if you are to enjoy the greatest pleasure in the collection and examination of fungi.

Do not pick more specimens than necessary at the time. Whenever possible, collect a young and full-grown specimen; if this is not possible, a recently matured specimen is best. They often grow side by side.

It is best to transport the fungi in a basket or container, placing the largest and heaviest at the bottom to prevent damage.

30a. MOREL. *Morchel'la esculen'ta* L. ex Fr.

Morels are among the few fungi appearing exclusively in the spring—April and May. The fungus prefers limestone country with a loamy soil rich in humus, and grows most readily under deciduous forests and in grassy places, especially on lime-rich dunes. The cap may be round, egg-shaped, or oval, and is holed like a sponge. The colour varies from ochre to brown, according to location and age. Both cap and stem are hollow. On the cap is the spore-forming hymenium.

The spores are in small sacs or asci, eight in each. The Morel thus belongs to the Sac fungi, or Ascomycetes. The yellowish stem, up to 3¼ inches long, is brittle and runs continuous with the cap. There are, however, species in which the cap is partly separated from the stalk, such as *M. rimocipes* DC.

The Morel has a pleasant smell and taste and in some countries is highly regarded as food, a fact recognised in the Latin specific name, *esculenta*: eatable.

30b. FIELD MOOR CLUB FUNGUS. *Clava'ria argilla'cea* Pers. ex Fr.

The name recalls two characteristics which make this fungus easy to find: it is distinctly club-shaped and grows in fields. It is also to be found at the edges of forests and on dunes.

The unbranched club, with its short stem, grows up to 2 inches tall and is cylindrical or slightly flattened in shape. It is cream to yellow in colour at first, later turning ochre. Usually several are to be found together, but they are not joined. It is very fragile and appears in summer and autumn. The spores are formed on the outside of the club. The Clavarias, or Club fungi, assume many shapes: there are branchless, few-branched, and many-branched species, coloured white, yellow, or orange.

30c. COLLARED EARTHSTAR. *Geas'trum triplex* Jungh.

This Earthstar is one of the biggest and the easiest to recognise. Very noticeable are the collar pieces between the inner part of the fruit-body (endoperidium) and the four to eight points of the star. This explains the Latin name, *triplex*: threefold. The fungus thus consists of three parts: the endoperidium containing the spores, the saucer-shaped collar or disc, and the exoperidium constituting the rays of the star. These characteristics are easily observed in a full-grown specimen. In its young state, the exoperidium entirely encloses the endoperidium, and no star-points are yet to be seen. The whole plant then has the appearance of a tulip bulb. With maturity, the outside skin opens from the top and splits into four or more star-points, which now bend outwards. The young plant is always underground, and young specimens can usually be found, if the soil is lightly disturbed, in the vicinity of an already discovered mature star.

Because the spores are formed inside the fruit-body, the Earth stars belong to the Gasteromycetes. When ripe, the spores escape through a small pore which opens in the top of the endoperidium. When a raindrop or anything else strikes the endoperidium, spores escape, as can be observed by flicking it with a finger. The colour is dirty white to light brown, at least in the young plant. Brittle at first, the Earthstar becomes leathery as it grows older, and at this latter stage there is often very little of the collar left. The collared variety is found in late summer and autumn, and old specimens may be met with even later in the year.

Wrap each species individually in a piece of paper (ideally, tissue paper), which should be carried already cut to size, and jot down on the paper (or separately with a key for identification) as many details as possible regarding the kind of soil, under what tree, whether growing on wood or not, on grassy plots, and so on. These details will quickly prove their usefulness. Apart from baskets, glass containers and all kinds of tins are recommended for easily damaged specimens. Do not throw the tissue away immediately you get home, as some spores may have fallen off; these can be of use in classifying the fungus without having recourse to a microscope. Use the packing material once only, as spores that may remain in the paper may mislead you the next time.

Keep your eyes not only on the ground but along the trunks of trees: there may be interesting fungi to be found there. Take a sharp knife in order to be able to collect the types which grow on trees.

Remove as much earth as possible from the lowest part of the stem; this saves packed specimens from becoming dirty. Be careful not to remove any part of the fungus, like the sac or pocket of *Amanita*. Dig out the whole fungus; many cases of food poisoning have occurred through too hasty and injudicious collecting.

Do not eat specimens attacked by maggots or those that are very old. With the exception of the Amanitas, do not be afraid to taste a piece of fungus now and again, but spit it out quickly after you have the taste.

Go at least once on an expedition with a more experienced mushroom expert or mycologist.

Make drawings of the specimens brought back home and also of their cross sections; make a note of all kinds of details in these drawings.

Form a collection of woody fungi—they are easily preserved, while other species present difficulties to the uninitiated.

It remains only for the author to hope that you will experience the same thrill as he on discovering toadstools about the green woods and fields on early summer mornings; and the same pleasure in returning home on golden autumn afternoons with fungi whose collection and classification will occupy many a long winter evening.

31a. WOOLLY DISC FUNGUS. *Scutelli'nia scutella'ta* (L. ex St. Amans) Lambotte, syn. *La'chnea scutella'ta* (L. ex St. Amans) Gillet, *Pezi'za scutella'ta* L. ex St. Amans.

Near the Great Orange Elf-cup Fungus (*Aleu'ria auran'-tia*), shown on page 134, we have also traced a great number of this ascomycete. This pretty little fungus grows on paper refuse. Its colour ranging from red lead to scarlet, the fungus is ½ inch wide and covered with stiff black and erect hairs at the margin. In its young stage the cap is closed and spherical-shaped; owing to the hairs, it is brownish-coloured. Later on it spreads out like a red saucer.

It grows on soil but also in groups on decaying wood.

31b. LITTLE BROWN ELF-CUP. *La'chnea hemispha'erica* (Wigg. ex Fr.) Gillet, syn. *Pezi'za hemispha'erica* Wigg. ex Fr.

The Little Brown Elf-cup—maximum diameter 1¼ inches—usually grows in groups, mostly on soil but also on decaying wood and vegetable mould. The cup or cupule shape of this fungus with an inrolled edge shows itself clearly in the young stage. It later expands, though it never becomes saucer-like.

The inside is a dirty white to grey, the outside yellow-brown and thickly covered with stiff brown hairs. This Sac fungus (Ascomycetes) is rather common in summer and autumn.

The Big Brown Elf-cup (*Galacti'nia ba'dia* [Pers. ex Fr.] Boud., syn. *Pezi'za ba'dia* Pers. ex Fr.), which may grow as large as 4¾ inches, is cupule-shaped at first but later becomes bowl- to saucer-shaped. Both the inside and the outside are dark brown.

31c. WHITE MORSEL-FUNGUS. *Helvel'la crispa* Scop. ex Fr.

The White Morsel-fungus belongs to the Sac fungi (Ascomycetes), and its bizarre shape is characteristic. The white stem—between 1¼ and 4 inches long—is covered with more or less irregular longitudinal ribs with, in between, deep and shallow pits and furrows which are grown together.

The cap, up to 1¼ inches wide, is yellowish white to cream-coloured with thin indented and wavy lobes. This easily breakable species is very common in pastures, on broad-leaved trees, and beside paths. It is to be found from summer until well into autumn, usually in groups.

The Black Morsel-fungus (*Helvella lacuno'sa* Afz. ex Fr.), with roughly the same general appearance, is usually somewhat smaller. The colour is mouse grey to grey-black, with a stem of a lighter hue. It can be found in about the same places as the white variety.

The way in which the spores are thrown out of their sacs or asci can be observed by tapping gently against the cap of a mature specimen of these species.

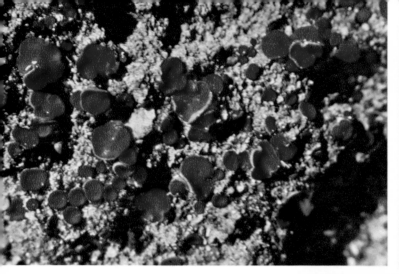

1a. *Amanita phalloides*
  b. *Amanita pantherina*
  c. *Amanita fulva*
2. *Polyporus squamosus*
3a. *Tricholoma sulphureum*
  b. *Cortinarius bolaris*
  c. *Cortinarius albo-violaceus*
  d. *Clitocybe nebularis*
4a. *Stereum hirsutum*
  b. *Phaeobulgaria inquinans*
  c. *Mycena galericulata*
  d. *Mycena haematopus*
5a. *Phlebia radiata*
  b. *Craterellus cornucopioides*
  c. *Hydnum repandum*
6a. *Phallus impudicus*
  b. *Mutinus caninus*
  c. *Leotia lubrica*
  d. *Helvella macropus*
7a. *Tremella foliacea*
  b. *Auricularia auricula-Judae*
  c. *Daedalea confragosa*
      (2 illustrations)
8a. *Polypilus frondosus*
  b. *Coriolus versicolor*
  c. *Laetiporus sulphureus*
9. *Mycena inclinata*
10a. *Piptoporus betulinus*
  b. *Lactarius chrysorheus*
  c. *Lactarius torminosus*
11a. *Oudemansiella mucida*

  b. *Kuehneromyces mutabilis*
  c. *Ramaria flava*
12. *Ganoderma applanatum*
13a. *Pholiota squarrosa*
  b. *Coprinus disseminatus*
  c. *Schizophyllum commune*
  d. *Gyroporus cyanescens*
14a. *Xylaria polymorpha*
  b. *Xylaria hypoxylon*
  c. *Coryne sarcoides*
15a. *Tricholomopsis rutilans*
  b. *Collybia maculata*
  c. *Polystictus perennis*
16a. *Suillus grevillei*
  b. *Suillus luteus*
  c. *Paxillus involutus*
17a. *Hapalopilus schweinitzii*
  b. *Sarcodon imbricatus*
  c. *Peniophora gigantea*
18a. *Masseeola crispa*
  b. *Auriscalpium vulgare*
  c. *Rhizopogon luteolus*
19a. *Gomphidius roseus*
  b. *Rhizina undulata*
  c. *Calocera viscosa*
20a. *Amanita muscaria*
  b. *Amanita muscaria*
  c. *Amanita muscaria*
21a. *Russula ochroleuca*
  b. *Russula emetica*
  c. *Clitocybe infundibuliformis*

22a. *Xerocomus parasiticus*
  b. *Scleroderma aurantium*
  c. *Cantharellus cibarius*
23a. *Hypholoma fasciculare*
  b. *Armillaria mellea*
24a. *Boletus edulis*
  b. *Stropharia aeruginosa*
  c. *Xerocomus subtomentosus*
25a. *Laccaria amethystina*
  b. *Crucibulum laeve*
  c. *Clavulina cristata*
26a, b. *Macrolepiota procera*
  c. *Lepiota acutesquamosa*
27a. *Coprinus comatus*
  b. *Coprinus plicatilis*
  c. *Agaricus campestris*
28a. *Calvatia uteriformis*
  b. *Geoglossum cookeianum*
  c. *Hygrophorus puniceus*
29a. *Myriostoma coliforme*
  b. *Lycoperdon perlatum*
  c. *Omphalotus olearius*
30a. *Morchella esculenta*
  b. *Clavaria argillacea*
  c. *Geastrum triplex*
31a. *Scutellinia scutellata*
  b. *Lachnea hemisphaerica*
  c. *Helvella crispa*
32a. *Peziza aurantia*
  b. *Verpa digitaliformis*
  c. *Galactinia vesiculosa*

32a. GREAT ORANGE ELF-CUP. *Pezi'za auran'tia* Pers. ex Fr., syn. *Aleu'ria auran'tia* (Pers. ex Fr.) Fuckel.

Especially with regard to colour, this species is one of the most striking representatives of the Sac fungi (Ascomycetes). Besides the vivid orange-red colour inside, this species is also remarkable for its size—up to 8 inches. The dish-shaped fungi will not be easily overlooked, particularly as many specimens are found growing together. The hymenium is spread out on the inside; the outside is a lighter orange and floury. The stem, if any, is very short. At a young stage the brittle fruit-body has not yet reached its saucer shape. The full-grown specimen has a more or less wavy or lobed edge, often turned in.

The species is fairly common and grows particularly on loamy and sandy spots in open woods, on forest tracks, at the sides of trenches, and often on sunny pasture land. The Orange Elf-cup can be found in early summer and also in the autumn. Among the orange-coloured Elf-cups, this species is the biggest and cannot be confused with any other species.

The specimens shown in the illustration grew on a loamy spot where refuse from a paper mill had been tipped.

32b. THIMBLE FUNGUS. *Ver'pa digita'liformis* Pers.

This little fungus is conspicuous for its shape rather than for its colour. It resembles a thimbled finger.

The genus *Verpa*, belonging to the Sac fungi (Ascomycetes), is closely related to the genus *Morchella* (Morel).

The cap is between ¾ and 1¾ inches wide and has a colour ranging from yellow-brown to brown. It is wrinkled and folded and connected to the stem only at the top.

The cylindrical, porous, whitish stem, up to 4 inches in length, soon becomes hollow and is granulated in texture. The whole fungus is brittle and very fragile.

The Thimble Fungus can be found in sparse woods, gardens, and under hedges, usually in spring, though it is not a common species.

32c. EARLY CUP-FUNGUS. *Galacti'nia vesiculo'sa* (Bull. ex Fr.) Le Gal., syn. *Aleu'ria vesiculo'sa* (Bull. ex Fr.) Gillet, *Pezi'za vesiculo'sa* Bull ex Fr.

The Early Cup-fungus is quite at home on refuse. It can be found, for instance, on manured spots, rich soil, and in gardens. The photographed specimens were growing on a rubbish heap consisting of cement, brick, mortar, etc. The sun, shining from the left into the cups, has produced the peculiar effect to be seen in the specimen on the lower right-hand side.

It grows close together in groups, has a short stem or none at all, and is a rather common species.

The cup, jug- to bladder-shaped at first, later opening up to ¾ to 4¾ inches wide, has a curved edge. The inside is brownish-yellow; the outside has a lighter tint and is covered with floury dust. When the mature specimens are touched, the escape of spores from the asci—like a cloud of dust—is clearly perceptible.

HABITATS

In the lists below, the species have been classified according to the most likely places where they may be found, as have also descriptions and illustrations. Note, however, that a great number of fungi may be found indifferently in deciduous forests, pinewoods, or in many other places. Some species are restricted to one kind of tree, such as the Oakhare (*Polypilus frondosus*) to the oak.

The species marked * grow on stems, trunks, branches, etc., often apparently on the soil, but in reality growing on buried wood or on the roots of trees. An example of such is the Honey Fungus (*Armillaria mellea*).

DECIDUOUS FOREST

Amanita fulva
— muscaria
— pantherina
— phalloides
— rubescens
Armillaria mellea*
Auricularia auricula-Judae*
Boletus edulis
Calocera cornea*
Calvatia uteriformis
Cantharellus cibarius
Clavulina cristata
Clitocybe flaccida
— infundibuliformis
— nebularis
Collybia fusipes*
Coprinus disseminata*
Coriolus versicolor*
Cortinarius albo-violaceus
— bolaris
Coryne sarcoides*
Craterellus cornucopioides
Crucibulum laeve*
Daedalea confragosa*
— quercina*
Flammulina velutipes*
Fomes igniarius*
Galactinia badia
Ganoderma applanatum*
Geastrum triplex
Gyroporus cyanescens
Helvella crispa
— lacunosa
— macropus
Hydnum repandum
Hypholoma fasciculare*
— sublateritium*
Kuehneromyces mutabilis*

Laccaria amethystina
— laccata
Lachnea hemisphaerica
Lactarius chrysorheus
— torminosus
Laetiporus sulphureus
Lenzites betulinus*
Leotia lubrica
Lepiota acutesquamosa
Lycoperdon perlatum
Macrolepiota procera
— rhacodes
Morchella esculenta
Mutinus caninus
Mycena galericulata*
— galopus*
— haematopus*
— inclinata*
— polygramma*
— pura
— sanguinolenta
Myriostoma coliforme
Omphalotus olearius*
Oudemansiella mucida
Paxillus involutus
Phaeobulgaria inquinans*
Phallus impudicus
Phlebia radiata*
Pholiota squarrosa*
Piptoporus betulinus*
Pleurotus ostreatus*
Polypilus frondosus*
— giganteus*
Polyporus squamosus*
Ramaria aurea
— flava
— formosa
Russula claroflava
— emetica
— fellea

Russula fragilis
— ochroleuca
— solaris
Schizophyllum commune*
Scleroderma aurantium
— verrucosum
Scutellinia scutellata*
Stereum hirsutum*
— purpureum*
Stropharia aeruginosa
Tremella foliacea*
Tricholoma saponaceum
— sulphureum
Ungulina fomentaria*
Verpa digitaliformis
Xerocomus chrysenteron
— subtomentosus
Xylaria hypoxylon*
— polymorpha*

PINE WOOD

Amanita fulva
— muscaria
— pantherina
— rubescens
— spissa
Armillaria mellea*
Auriscalpium vulgare*
Boletus edulis
Calocera viscosa*
Cantharellus cibarius
Clitocybe flaccida
— infundibuliformis
— clavipes
Collybia maculata
Crucibulum laeve*
Flammulina velutipes*
Fomes annosus*
Galactinia badia

Gomphidius roseus
Gyroporus cyanescens
Hapalopilus schweinitizii*
Hirschioporus abietinus*
Hydnum repandum
Hygrophoropsis aurantiaca
Hygrophorus hypothejus
Hypholoma capnoides*
— fasciculare*
Kuehneromyces mutabilis*
Laccaria amethystina
— laccata
Lachnea hemisphaerica
Lactarius deliciosus
Lepiota acutesquamosa
Macrolepiota rhacodes
Marasmius scorodonius
Masseeola crispa*
Mutinus caninus
Mycena galericulata*
— galopus*
— polygramma*
— sanguinolenta
Paxillus involutus
Peniophora gigantea*
Phallus impudicus
Pholiota squarrosa*
Polystictus perennis
Ramaria aurea
— flava
— formosa
Rhizina undulata
Rhizopogon luteolus
Russula emetica
— fragilis
— ochroleuca
Sarcodon imbricatus
Schizophyllum commune*
Scleroderma aurantium
Stropharia aeruginosa

Suillus bovinus
— granulatus
— grevilleii
— luteus
— piperatus
Tremella foliacea*
Tremellodon gelatinosum*
Tricholoma flavovirens
— saponaceum
Tricholomopsis rutilans*
Tylopilus felleus
Xerocomus badius
— chrysenteron
— subtomentosus

MIXED WOOD

Amanita fulva
— muscaria
— pantherina
— phalloides
— rubescens
Armillaria mellea*
Boletus edulis
Cantharellus cibarius
Clavulina cristata
Clitocybe clavipes
— infundibuliformis
— nebularis
Craterellus cornucopioides
Crucibulum laeve*
Galactinia badia
Geastrum triplex
Gyroporus cyanescens
Hygrophoropsis aurantiaca
Hypholoma fasciculare*
Kuehneromyces mutabilis*
Laccaria amethystina
— laccata

Lachnea hemisphaerica
Leotia lubrica
Lepiota acutesquamosa
Lycoperdon perlatum
Macrolepiota procera
— rhacodes
Mycena galopus*
— polygramma*
— pura
— sanguinolenta
Paxillus involutus
Phallus impudicus
Pholiota squarrosa*
Ramaria aurea
— flava
— formosa
Russula emetica
— fragilis
— ochroleuca
Schizophyllum commune*
Scleroderma aurantium
— verrucosum
Scutellinia scutellata*
Stropharia aeruginosa
Tremella foliacea*
Tricholoma sulphureum
Xerocomus chrysenteron
— subtomentosus

OPEN PLACES AND MEADOWS

Agaricus arvensis
— campestris
Calocybe georgii
Calvatia uteriformis
Clavaria argillacea
Clavulina cristata
Clitocybe flaccida

Coprinus comatus
— plicatilis
Galactinia vesiculosa
Geastrum triplex
Geoglossum cookeianum
Helvella crispa
— lacunosa
Hygrophorus coccineus
— miniatus
— puniceus
Laccaria amethystina
— laccata
Lachnea hemisphaerica
Lepiota acutesquamosa
Lycoperdon perlatum
Macrolepiota procera
— rhacodes
Marasmius oreades
Morchella esculenta
Mutinus caninus
Myriostoma coliforme
Panaeolus campanulatus
Paxillus involutus
Peziza aurantia
Scleroderma aurantium
— verrucosum
Scutellinia scutellata and*
Stropharia aeruginosa
Verpa digitaliformis
Xerocomus chrysenteron

BIRCH

Amanita muscaria
Lactarius torminosus
Lenzites betulinus*
Phlebia radiata*
Russula claroflava

BEECH

Collybia fusipes*
Cortinarius albo-violaceus
— bolaris
Coryne sarcoides*
Ganoderma applanatum*
Oudemansiella mucida*
Phaeobulgaria inquinans*
Polypilus giganteus*
Ramaria formosa
Russula fellea
— solaris

OAK

Amanita phalloides
Collybia fusipes*
Daedalea quercina*
Lactarius chrysorheus
Mycena inclinata*
Phaeobulgaria inquinans*
Polypilus frondosus*

LARCH

Suillus grevilleii

ELDER

Auricularia auricula-Judae*

HEATH

Clavaria argillacea
Lycoperdon perlatum
Scleroderma aurantium
Suillus bovinus

EDIBLE SPECIES

Young specimens are preferable for human consumption since the older species are usually grub-eaten. Before preparing the fungi for cooking, check once again to make quite certain of identification. Toadstools should not be gathered for eating without considerable knowledge of the species. No attempt to have just one taste should be made without absolute and complete certainty of identification.

The species listed below are those that have been dealt with in this book.

Agaricus arvensis
— *campestris*
Armillaria mellea
   (without stems)

Boletus edulis
Cantharellus cibarius
Clitocybe nebularis
Coprinus comatus
   (young)

Hydnum repandum
Lactarius deliciosus
Macrolepiota procera
— *rhacodes*
Morchella esculenta

Tricholoma flavovirens
Xerocomus badius
— *chrysenteron*
— *subtomentosus*

POISONOUS SPECIES

But for a single exception, all Amanitas are poisonous.

Amanita muscaria
— *pantherina*
— *phalloides* (deadly)
Clitocybe olearia

Lactarius torminosus
Ramaria formosa
   (purging)
Russula emetica

Russula fragilis (listed as poisonous because of its strong resemblance to R. emetica)

Scleroderma aurantium
— *verrucosum*

PARASITES

Armillaria mellea
Ganoderma applanatum
Hapalopilus schweinitzii

Laetiporus sulphureus
Masseeola crispa
Oudemansiella mucida

Pholiota squarrosa
Piptoporus betulinus
Polypilus frondosus

Polypilus giganteus
Rhizina undulata

GLOSSARY

abietinus	pertaining to the fir	*cookeianum*	referring to the mycologist M. C. Cooke	*haematopus*	with bloodfoot (stalk)
acutesquamosa	pointed scaled			*hemisphaerica*	semi-spherical
aeruginosa	verdigris-coloured	*cornea*	hornish	*hirsutum*	haired
albo-violaceus	white-violet	*cornucopioides*	resembling the horn of plenty	*hypothejus*	sulphur-coloured at the base
amesilthystina	amethyst-coloured	*crispa*	frizzed	*hypoxylon*	woody at the base
annosus	living for years	*cristata*	crested, resembling a crest	*igniarius*	belonging to fire
applanatum	flattened			*illudens*	misleading
argillacea	loam-coloured, yellowish white	*cyanescens*	turning dark blue	*imbricata(us)*	tile-wise
		deliciosus	tasty	*impudicus*	impudent
arvensis	growing in fields	*digitaliformis*	thimble-shaped	*inclinata*	curved
aurantia	orange-coloured	*disseminata*	as though sown	*inflata*	inflated
aurantiaca(um)	orange	*edulis*	edible	*infundibuliformis*	funnel-shaped
aurea	golden	*elegans*	graceful	*inquinans*	staining
auricula-Judae	Jew's Ear	*emetica*	emetic	*inversa*	reversed
auriscalpium	earspoon	*equestre*	pertaining to a knight	*involutus*	inrolled
badia	auburn			*laccata*	sealing wax
betulina(us)	pertaining to the birch	*esculenta*	palatable	*lacunosa*	furrowed
		fasciculare	forming bundles	*laeve*	smooth, without hairs
bolare(is)	brick-red	*fellea*	bitter as gall		
bovinus	pertaining to the ox	*flaccida*	slack	*lutea(us)*	yellow
		flava	yellowish, golden	*luteolus*	yellowish
bovista	derived from the German popular name Pfofist	*flavovirens*	leaf-like	*macropus*	with a long foot (stalk)
		fomentaria	used for tinder		
		formosa	beautiful	*maculata*	with spots
caelatum	engraved	*fragilis*	brittle, breakable	*mellea*	honey-coloured
campanulatus	bell-shaped	*frondosus*	having many leaves (caps)	*miniatus*	red-lead
campester(ris)	growing in the fields			*mucida*	slimy
		fulva	ruddy, yellow-brown	*muscaria*	connected with flies
caninus	canine				
capnoides	resembling smoke, smokegrey	*fusipes*	with a spindle foot	*mutabilis*	changeable
				nebularis	connected with fog, fog-coloured
chrysenteron	golden interior	*galericulata(us)*	with bonnet or helmet		
chrysorheus	flowing gold (milk)	*galopus*	with milkfoot (stalk)	*ochroleuca*	yellow-white
				olearia	connected with oil (olive)
cibarius	edible	*gelatinosum*	gelatinous		
cirrhata	curled	*gemmata*	pearled	*ophioglossoides*	resembling a serpent's tongue
claroflava	bright yellow	*georgii*	referring to St. George's Day (early in the year)		
clavipes	clubfoot			*oreades*	mountain nymphs (fairies)
coccineus	scarlet red				
coliforme	sieve-shaped			*ostreatus*	oyster-shaped
columbetta	little dove	*granulatus*	granulated	*pantherina*	marked like a panther
comatus	tufted	*grevilleii*	referring to the mycologist R. K. Greville		
commune	common			*parasiticus*	parasitising
confragosa	rough, rugged			*perennis*	perennial, living a long time

perlatum	pearled	*rubescens*	turning red	*sublateritium*	brick-reddish
phalloides	phallic	*rutilans*	yellowish red	*subtomentosus*	somewhat felty
piperatus	pepperish	*sanguinolenta*	bloody, blood-red	*sulphureum(us)*	sulphur-coloured
plicatilis	with folds	*saponaceum*	soapy	*torminosus*	producing
polymorpha	multi-shaped	*sarcoides*	fleshy, flesh-		cramps, gripes
procera	slender, tall		coloured	*triplex*	threefold, triple
puniceus	purple-red	*schweinitzii*	referring to the	*undulata*	waved
pura	pure, clean		mycologist of	*uteriformis*	bladder-shaped
pupureum	purple-red, purple		that name	*vaginata*	with vagina
quercina	pertaining to the	*scorodonius*	smelling of garlic	*velutipes*	with a velvet
	oak	*scutellata*	saucer-shaped		foot
radiata	radially	*solaris*	pertaining to the	*verrucosa(um)*	warty
	constructed		sun	*versicolor*	multi-coloured,
repandum	scalloped, curved	*spectabilis*	beautiful		variegated
rhacodes	as if covered with	*spissa*	close together	*vesiculosa*	bladder-like
	rags	*squamosa*	scaled	*viscosa*	sticky
rimosipes	with a split foot	*squarrosa*	covered with	*vulgare*	common,
	(stem)		scales		appearing
roseus	pinkish red	*stricta*	stiff		everywhere

BIBLIOGRAPHY

BULLER, A. H. R. *Researches on Fungi*, Vol. I, London, 1909.

LE CERF, R. *Cent Champignons*, Paris, n.d.

CHARLES, V. K. *Some Common Mushrooms and How to Know Them*. U.S.D.A. Circular 143, Washington, D.C., 1946.

CHRISTENSEN, C. M. *Common Edible Mushrooms*, Newton Center, Massachusetts, 1959.

— *Common Fleshy Fungi*. Minneapolis, Minn., 1955.

COOL, C., & VAN DER LEK, H. A. A. *Paddestoelenboek*, Amsterdam, I, 1936; II, 1944.

LE GAL, M. *Promenades Mycologiques*, Paris, 1957.

GAMS, H. *Kleine Kryptogamenflora*, Band IIb, *Blätter und Bauchpilze*, 2nd edition, Stuttgart, 1955.

GRAMBERG, E. *Pilze der Heimat*, 2 vols., Leipzig, 1939.

HAAS, H., *Pilze Mitteleuropas, Speisepilze*, Stuttgart, 1951; *Speisepilze II und Giftpilze*, Stuttgart, 1953.

HEIM, R. *Les Champignons d'Europe*, 2 parts, Paris, 1957.

HESLER, F. R. *Mushrooms of the Great Smokies*, Nashville, 1960.

INGOLD, C. T. *Dispersal in Fungi*, London, 1953.

JACCOTTET, J., & ROBERT, P. *Les Champignons dans la Nature*, Neuchâtel, 1925.

JAHN, H. *Pilze Rundum*, Hamburg, 1951.

KONRAD, P., & MAUBLANC, A. *Les Agaricales*, Paris, 1948.

KUHNER, R., & ROMAGNESI, H. *Flore Analytique des Champignons Supérieurs (Agarics, Boletes, Chantarelles)*, Paris, 1953.

MAUBLANC, A. *Les Champignons de France*, 2 parts, 3rd edition, Paris, 1946.

MICHAEL-HENNIG., *Handbuch für Pilzfreunde*, 1st part printed, Jena, 1958

MICHAEL-SCHULZ, *Führer für Pilzfreunde*, 3 parts, Leipzig, 1927–39.

PILAT, A., & OTTO USAK. *A Handbook of Mushrooms*, London, 1960.

— *Mushrooms*, English ed., London.

POSTMA, W. P., & Kleijn, H. *Paddestoelen*, Haarlem, 1952.

RAMSBOTTOM, J. *Mushrooms and Toadstools*, London and New York, 1953.

RAU, W. *Unsere Pilze*, Heidelberg, 1951.

REA, C. *British Basidiomycetae*, Cambridge, 1922.

RICKEN, A. *Die Blätterpilze*, Leipzig, 1951.

— *Vademecum für Pilzfreunde*, 2nd edition, Leipzig, 1920.

SMITH, A. H. *The Mushroom Hunter's Field Guide*, 2nd edition, Michigan, 1958.

THOMAS, W. S. *Field Book of Common Mushrooms*, 3rd ed., New York, 1948.

STRICKER, P. *Das Pilzbuch*, Karlsruhe, 1949.

SWANENBURG DE VEYE, G. D. *Paddestoelen*, Naarden, 1950.

VAN DER VEN, D. J. *Het Wondere Leven der Paddestoelen*, Amsterdam, 1915.

DE VRIES, G. A. *Paddestoelen*, Zutphen, 1955.

WAKEFIELD, E. M. *Common Fungi*, London, 1954.

— *The Observer's Book of Common Fungi*, London and New York, 1958.

— & DENNIS, W. G. *Common British Fungi*, London, 1950.

VAN DER ZEE-KRUSEMAN, M., & WITTOP KONING, M. *Paddestoelen Zoeken en Eten*, Rotterdam, 1948.

ZEITLMAYER, L. *Knaurs Pilzbuch*, Munich, 1955.